Fractured:
A Hug Your Chaos Story of
Healing

Healing From Addiction, Illness & Disease
Through Energy Work

Author: Lindsay Carricarte-Jones
Cover Art: Lillian Tseng
© 2017 Hug Your Chaos

Kristin -
You are a Badass!
Can't wait to watch you
give your message to the
world! ♡
Lindsay

Dedication

To each and every single person that has crossed my path in this life, I thank you. You have each played a role in my own journey in some way.

To my Mom and Dad, I especially thank and honor you for bringing me into this world and for giving me every experience I needed in order to come to the place that I now stand. You have shown me what it is to be human and what it is to show up for family through thick and thin. Without you this book would not have been possible.

To Myrra, thank you for being the first person in my life to tell me that I could challenge my own belief systems. The day you asked, "Why do you believe what you believe?" ignited a process inside me that fueled my healing journey.

To Iona, you were the guiding light in my most darkest hour. You taught me more about who I wanted to be in the world and showed me it was possible each and every day. I thank you.

To my amazing editor, Lois Person, thank you, thank you, thank you! You were the icing on the cake of Fractured.

To my astrological sister and graphic design ninja, Lillian Tseng, what can I say that you don't already know. As always, you nail my inner vision.

To those who still suffer from disconnection, it is for you I wrote. I see you and I feel you. You can change your life.

To my soul sister, Alanna, thank you for being you. Your dedication and drive in your own life mission has inspired and kept me going more than you know!

Last, but never least, my Twin Flame, my Christopher. For everything I am and all that I am becoming, I thank you. Without you I could never have achieved the depths of expansion and healing that have contributed to this book. I love you madly, my sweet.

Table of Contents

Introduction

This book has been a long time in the making. It is one part introductory information about the chakra system, which balances the human body, mind, and spirit; one part my own personal story and life experiences; and one part a manual of practices that can bring us to a state of connection, unification, and balance. By balance I mean a state that is free from fractures within the self *and* free from fractures that would separate us from Source. This is the Hug Your Chaos way.

My life was one of chaos, pain, and suffering that came in many forms and manifestations which presented as dis-ease of my physical body, illness of my mind and emotional body, and disconnect from my spiritual body. I was never able to see just how obvious it is that, to be whole, complete, and well, we must balance and unify the mind, body, and spirit within the self so we may reconnect with our Higher Being and ultimately reconnect with Source.

This is a manual for living that offers insight and information into the aspects of the triad—mind, body, and soul. I briefly introduce the main components and functions of the three: the body with the chakra system, along with its various parts and main functions; the mind on the level of intellect, conscious, subconscious, emotion, and ego; and the spirit, as our divine and true nature. It is also a memoir and a beacon of hope where I share the chaos and pain of my life through illness and addiction, depression and misery, to where I found a life of balance and harmony, so others may find it when they are ready for their own paradigm shift. I don't know that finding a book like this would have woken me up before I was ready, but who's to say. It's with the hope of planting a seed that I share my travels through hell and despair—from disconnection to wholeness—so someone may pick it up and say, "*Hey, me too! I feel that...perhaps there is a different way. Maybe I can Hug My Chaos too*"

Lastly, it is an introductory outline to the practices that have saved my life and brought me to an entirely new and different place of living...one I never would have thought possible a few short years ago. It's a guide to one of the paths that leads out of the dark chaos of the mind and ego; the path that worked—and is still working—for me.

This book is about my experiences and practices as they have helped me on my journey. I am the expert on this because I am the only one who has directly lived the story that unfolds here. I do not claim to have all the answers, nor do I believe that my way is "right" and others "wrong." Fractured simply "is" the story of my life of chaos and imbalance to my life of peace, harmony, and love. It is the story of Hugging My Chaos in order to heal.

For the purposes of conveying my point and describing certain things, I am forced to use certain words and phrases that are quite limiting in their ability to accurately describe or explain what I have experienced. But, alas, as these words are all we have to communicate with in this dimension, I must use them. If you are one who is apt to cling to literal meanings of words–and cling to a "this or that" or a "black and white" mentality, so to speak–you may want to pause before reading. Pause and forget everything you think you know and approach this from a place of new beginnings and freshness. Life is full of paradoxes and ironies; contradictions abound in the Higher Realms. It is because we try to understand everything with the mind and limited human intellect in this realm that we get frustrated and want to discount anything the mind cannot understand. So I ask you, just while you read, to let go of the idea that this book is going to help you understand anything intellectually. It won't. Or it may here and there. But forget that and aim higher. Aim to come to the end of it with a new understanding in your heart and soul—a deeper understanding that arises from the place which exists beyond the mind. Create some space within before you read on. Take a few deep breaths, sit up straight, come into your body, and leave your mind. If you would like to embark on a journey of your own chakra healing with me, visit www.hugyourchaos.com/coaching to discover the various programs and courses I offer.

Enjoy, dear one, and namasté.

Fractured

4

Section 1
The Physical Body

Fractured

Chapter 1
The Physical Body and the Chakras

"Movement is a medicine for creating change in a person's physical, emotional, and mental states." ~Carol Welch

As humans, we are made up of three bodies—the physical, the mental/emotional, and the spiritual. There are, well and truly, more etheric and astral bodies that exist, but for the purposes of this book we only need to focus on the three mentioned here. Let's not complicate everything right from the start. When these three bodies are connected, aligned, and operating in a state of balance we operate at our highest potential. We find that harmony and joy come naturally, and that discord and hatred do not.

Let us begin on the physical plane of the triad, aka the human body. The most fundamental point of identification for us. Most of us identify so deeply with our physical form, as though it is all that defines us, we forget that we are made up of other bodies and layers as well. The physical body is the only body that is dense enough for us to see and touch, so this is where we can visibly see many manifestations of a fractured, blocked, or unbalanced system. It's usually the first place visible, tangible symptoms of blockages manifest. At least it sure was in my case, which is part of what I'm going to share with you shortly.

Often times, we get so stuck in the physical/material realm that we forget there is so much more to living life on planet Earth. It doesn't help that our modern society sort of perpetuates this erroneous belief on top of our own inherent human tendency to forget we are spiritual beings. I know I sure did for a very long time! For years I could not see outside the realm of the material world and the physical body. I was ensnared in all things physical. I was so close minded, I would not even consider there was more to life. Realistically, I just didn't even bother to think about it.

Funnily enough, when I finally came to see the bigger picture, I began unearthing the buried knowledge inside. This is where it all started to make perfect sense to me, deep within, as though I already knew it. I'm getting ahead of myself though. We will come back to that because, first, we must explore how to even identify the blocks, *especially* on a physical level. So returning to my pre-knowing fractured state, there were many years that I could not even begin to fathom just how infinite we are as spiritual beings. It wasn't until I was able to balance mind, body, and spirit–thus opening to the belief that we are so much more than just our physical forms– that I was able to start seeing and understanding the true and deep nature of all that is. Therefore, because the chakra system is what makes connection and communication between the spiritual body and physical form possible, I am going to start here.

I must add that this is not a textbook, and I am no doctor of anything. All I have to offer is my own working experience and knowledge, so I will give a basic introduction to the chakra system, as I understand it, for the purpose of understanding the examples and points of discussion that I raise in my story. This is so you, my dear reader, can identify and see how these very same issues, blocks, and problems show up in your life. And so that you can see there is hope and healing for anyone who is ready to dig in and do some work. (Visit www.hugyourchaos.com/coaching to find out how I can help you in your healing journey.)

I believe that books, like people, come to us at the perfect time, with a purpose to either bring awareness to something we need to see or further guide us on our path. So if you are ready for this information–as I was when it came to me–it may awaken a deeper knowing; one you already carry deep within your greater consciousness. When I started studying chakras and meditation, I felt this deep knowing within; I felt it awaken just as you may too. It felt as though the information was an old home, and I was returning to it after a very long time away. *It just made sense to me.* By this point of my journey, I had escaped the prison of my mind and the physical constraints of addiction and was beginning to cultivate a quiet space of balance inside. This allowed my higher self to be heard from where she resides in the realm of the collective consciousness. We will get to that process later, so if you aren't quite there yet, and you are just looking for something more, for answers or a new way of living, then not to worry! I speak to you, my dear ones, no matter where you stand on this path of healing and self-reflection. We are all in this together, and I was once where you stand. Consider that your pep talk because now we get right into business with a little bit of educational stuff peppered with some juicy and scandalous anecdotes from my life to illustrate the problems that arise from energetic blocks.

In case you aren't familiar with chakras, we will start with a little introduction. Chakra is a Sanskrit word meaning "wheel". Essentially, this is exactly what the chakras are–spinning wheels of energy. Chakra work has become an amazingly beautiful and integral part of my life, as well as the fundamental element of my life purpose, which is to help others find their way to healing through chakra work and meditation. The chakra system is a very complex and multi-layered realm that continues to deepen the more I work with it. For the purposes of this book, we have seven major chakras that I will refer to. They are split between three lower and three higher with the heart center in the middle, which serves as the bridge between lower and higher self.

Each of the seven major chakras corresponds with specific organs, behaviors, emotions, body systems, and human developments. Thus, it makes sense, as we delve into the specifics, that we will see how the lower chakras correspond with our very immature, child-like, and selfish tendencies. We will also see how traumas in early life may derail and block the function of the lower system, thus skewing our entire inner balance. Liken this to four wheels on a vehicle where, if one is off-center, the other tires end up worn out. The same goes in the chakra system. What happens when a tire is out of alignment, and you keep driving on it? Bang! Eventually you end up with a flat, useless tire.

The first three chakras, grouped as the lower system, govern our fundamental emotions and needs. Like I said, this can show up as very immature and child-like behavior when unchecked or blocked. The higher chakras, five through seven, are the centers of higher living as well as home to our mental and spiritual aspirations and faculties. The middle chakra (fourth), found at heart center, is the balancing point. The idea of a properly balanced and functioning system is connection of mind, body, and spirit, which results in the upward flow of the heavy, dense energies of the lower system.

In a properly functioning system, this heavy dense energy flows upward to the higher chakras where it can be balanced out by higher density vibrations and emotions. We will get into more detail in the mind/emotion section of the book. For a basic understanding think in terms of energy. Emotions such as anger, jealousy, guilt, fear, and sadness are heavy and dense, while happiness, joy, gratitude, and love are free-flowing, light, high vibration energies. Just like in stagnant water, which doesn't flow, all the mucky, heavy crap settles on the bottom. The same goes with our inner energy flow! If our energy isn't flowing through, all that heavy crap settles in and festers there. More often than not in my life, the physical symptoms of this stuck and stagnant energy would manifest much more quickly than any other symptoms of imbalance.

Let's visualize for a moment. Imagine an unbalanced system. There's dense energy swirling around the lower chakras: maybe excessive, maybe deficient. Perhaps it's completely stagnant and stuck. All things related to emotions, needs, wants, survival, self-esteem, safety, and security are located down here. All those very human elements that we equate with survival. In other words, our *needs*. To put it simply, in a healthy system all of this stuff would be channeled upward into the heart, where it would be greeted with love and compassion in order for transmutation and healing to occur, and then channeled further upward into the higher realms of the spirit—the realm of the higher self.

In a well-balanced system, when this lower vibration energy is transmuted and set free, we act in love, harmony, and balance instead of anger, hate, and intolerance. Now see a block in that heart center where the energy flow isn't taking place. The flow may be sluggish, murky, or non-existent. Like water in a pool that has a broken filter, we are going to quickly become, muddy, murky, heavy, and selfish, bogged down by our needs, wants, and desires. We will cease to operate from love and kindness. As a result, all of the physical things that latch us to the material/physical world become all we can see. And now we get to the good part. *THIS* is what I'm going to illustrate in this book—scenarios I have collected from working with others as well as my own scintillating personal saga in order to outline the problems caused by energetic imbalance.

So let's get to it. As I said, the chakras are basically the energy centers of our physical bodies. We have many all over the human body, but there are seven major ones I am going to introduce here. Since this is a book dedicated to provoking thought and consideration for practical life application and improvement, I am not going to harp on too much with histories and scientific fact that will just get in the way of the practical application. Our aim here, during our time together, is to get you identifying with my struggles so that you can then shine light on your own in order to heal and align your own blocks and fractures. I am not looking to overwhelm with intellectual facts, but merely to present a very living adaptation of chakra work and balanced living. If anyone is inclined to read further on a deeper level, I am including a comprehensive and thorough reading list of wonderful resources which helped me at the start of my journey. You can find more factual and intellectual information there.

Now, we all know our physical bodies exist, right? We see them, we control them, we hurt them, we move them, and we feel all of it. We watch them grow, stretch, change, and age. They get sick, they feel good, and they get injured. No argument there, right? Now what if I said I believe that we are not just our physical body? That from my experience I have come to understand there is so much more to us as human beings than just our physical forms. Our bodies are our homes, so we must take care of them. Yet we often realize this fact too late and we are already suffering from sickness, weight issues, lethargy, atrophy, illness, dis-ease, discomfort, and poisoning from our stuck energy.

The physical body is just one-third of the equation that makes us whole. The physical body is our means of walking, talking, and living a human experience and it is where problems rooted in energetic imbalance often manifest first and most obviously. I am going to liken the chakra system to portals or gateways… communication hubs between our physical, emotional and spiritual bodies. Like the place far on the horizon where the sun, sky, and land meet at sunset.

Chakra study, meditation, and knowledge have been around for centuries. The ancient Hindu yogis have been aware of the power and importance of chakra system balance for thousands of years. Ancient texts outline points of the body and what these points control. So it's not just some New-Age mumbo jumbo, as I once thought, and as I have been accused of endorsing. It's all much older than our Western religions. Funnily enough, even Christian texts (when you get away from the dogma) refer to vital and important energy points of the body which hold the key to enlightenment, self-realization, and Christ consciousness. That being said, this, of course, is *not* a religious text, it's a life text. It's a practical application and illustration of how ancient teachings have manifested and played a part in my life in order to show how, by energetically balancing my system, I have overcome many self-imposed blocks and limitations in order to live my most heart-centered and abundant life.

If you can, imagine the chakras as spinning discs of energy at various points up and down the spinal column—this will help your understanding if you are a visual person. The seven we will talk about are placed beginning in the lower sacral region of the body and move up to the crown of the head. Keep in mind that we can suffer from overactive or underactive energy imbalances in each chakra, which results in excessive or deficient energies wreaking havoc in our system. This all manifests as extreme behaviors and, you guessed it, illness and physical dis-ease. There may be blockages, as I will describe in my personal case, which resulted in splits–or fractures–among aspects of my system. This is basically a fracture among the physical, emotional/mental, and spiritual bodies where there is no working connection. We will talk about some examples of imbalances and blocks, and I will share my personal examples with you.

**I created a special facebook community to share chakra knowledge here: www.facebook.com/groups.chakrachaos*

Now let's meet the chakras!

Muladhara - Root Chakra

Starting at the base of the spine we find the Muladhara, or Root, Chakra. Its element is Earth, and this is where we root and connect to the energy of Earth, our true biological mother. From here we ground and draw our strength. Muladhara's color is red and this is the home of Kundalini energy, a very powerful creative force that is not to be played with. The Root is the center of survival, to put it bluntly; this is where adrenaline in the face of danger comes from, and also the human fight or flight response. Our base human instincts are governed in Muladhara and it is the center of trust, grounding, stability, survival, and self-preservation. In a balanced system, the Muladhara will support presence in the moment, stability, and a sense of security on the physical plane. In other words, *we feel safe.* In an unbalanced system someone with overactive Muladhara may be possessive, greedy, inflexible, fearful of many things, selfish, materialistic and/or stubborn, and not willing to see higher or greater meaning in life.

My imbalance here showed up in that I couldn't see past the materialistic plane when it came to my needs and my security. I was as stubborn as a mule, selfish, inconsiderate, and lived in straight up survival mode for years. Don't worry, I will share those gritty details later. Someone with an underactive Muladhara may be insecure, ungrounded, nervous, feel homeless no matter where they are, feel unwelcome around others, and/or always find themselves in victim mentality. In other words, an inability to root and ground no matter how conducive the surrounding environment is. Early emotional traumas like abandonment, rejection, and abuse may drastically unbalance Muladhara energy, which then manifests in fearful, needy, clingy, emotional behaviors.

The system will try to correct unbalanced Muladhara energy with a counteractive dose of Sahasrara energy (ego, intellect). For example, those who operate from pure intellect, ego, and constant need of tangible proof, may have excessive Sahasrara to counteract deficient Muladhara, and vice versa. Muladhara governs the prostate gland, kidneys, bladder, and spine, as well as regulating mechanisms of the physical body and governing the sense of smell. Those always keen to "sniff out a rat," that don't trust anything they can't touch or prove, may benefit from balancing and healing this chakra.

Svadhisthana - Sacral Chakra

Next up, we come to the Svadhisthana, or Sacral, Chakra, around the area of the reproductive organs behind the naval. This spinning orange energy center is linked to the element of water and our emotions. It is the home of our fluidity and flexibility. Svadhishthana governs relationships, sexuality, empathy, pleasure, and well-being; it is also where we balance masculine and feminine energies.

Also rooted in survival, this is where our needs, wants, creativity, and desires come from. In a balanced system, Svadhisthana energy gives us feelings of delight, enjoyment, balance, and an open flow of emotions. Our sense of ego (self), others, and family–and, thus, perceived separation from these–is derived from this chakra. Balanced Svadhisthana gives a healthy and humble sense of self and surroundings. Someone with an overactive or excessive Svadhisthana energy may be manipulative, jealous, impulsive, controlling, overly-emotional, addictive, and/or lustful. Problems like having no respect for the boundaries of others are rooted here.

One with underactive or deficient Svadhisthana may be co-dependent, closed off to others, submissive, a martyr, emotionally shut-down, non-feeling, cold, and/or selfish. I mentioned earlier the inclination towards being very childish and concerned only with self, like a two-year old—this was me.

I suffered from a massively underactive Svadhisthana for much of my life, which resulted in a complete block of my emotions. I wasn't just closed off to others, but to myself as well. I felt threatened all the time, out of touch, jaded, bitter, and hateful from all of my trapped emotions. I didn't care who I hurt. I didn't care what happened to me. But, again, we will get into that later. The system will try to correct unbalanced Svadhisthana with its higher counterpart—Ajna. This resulted in my suffering from an overactive intellect and underactive emotional capacity. Kind of a nightmare to be around unless you want a robot for a friend!

Svadhisthana governs the reproductive systems, gonads, legs, all fluid systems (blood, lymph, saliva, tears, urine), and sense of taste. Its corresponding organ is the tongue. Emotional eaters may suffer from an unbalanced energy here, while balanced Svadhisthana helps us embrace a healthy body image, acceptance of our sexuality, and the beauty in all of our physical gifts as part of our human make-up. Modern society has taught us a lot of shame around our inherent sexual nature, resulting in much unbalanced Svadhisthana energy in the world. Early emotional and sexual trauma may also severely unbalance this energy. Denial and suppression of one's sexual inclinations or urges would also unbalance Svadhisthana, as would denying one's inner masculine or feminine energies.

We need balance within if we want balance without. We all carry masculine and feminine within, so denial of either of these streams of energy can block this chakra. Trying to fit into the well intentioned gender identity and roles dictated by societal 'norms' often end up doing more harm than good and skew the energy here.

Manipura - Solar Plexus Chakra

Moving up to the solar plexus region, we come to the wheel of the Manipura Chakra, the center for power, control, self-worth, discipline, and self-control. This is your center to make shit happen. Manipura is linked to the element of fire, its color is yellow, and, as mentioned, it is a powerhouse chakra; a dominant energy and fuel center within us. The last of our lower density "human nature" chakras, it is also the center for joy, motivation, transformation, vitality, self-esteem, and energy. It can cause major problems when blocked and/or unbalanced. This is the center of conversion where we convert all things ingested, be they food or ideas, into usable forms of energy for our optimum function.

Balanced Manipura governs a true sense of self-esteem in a humble, realistic, and non-egotistical way, if you can imagine this. A healthy sense of self, if you will. It's a bit of a radical idea in today's world. When this center is balanced and flowing, Manipura energy helps us find complete satisfaction in all that we do, along with a sense of contentment and serenity in life. Unrefined emotions and our natural ability to create what we want in the physical form flow from Manipura.

Because it is so powerful, unbalanced Manipura energy naturally wreaks havoc in our lives. Trust me, I suffered from excessive and overactive Manipura energy for most of my life, and it was a force to be reckoned with. As it did in my case, it may manifest as egotism; self-absorbed and selfish thinking and actions; detrimentally ambitious drive to succeed; a lack of respect for boundaries of others; or aggressive, controlling, domineering, and combative behaviors. In reality, yes, I was an asshole. Not exactly a list of prime character traits you'd want in a friend, is it?

As you will learn shortly, I was a nightmare to be around. I was overbearing and rigid, unyielding in every way possible. My way or the highway. Take it or leave it. I didn't have an ounce of energy or desire to deal with anyone or anything that wasn't as I wished it to be. If I didn't like it, off I went. And I might just run you over in the process of leaving.

On the flip side, the deficient or underactive Manipura may show up as a poor sense of self-worth, extremely low self-esteem, over-sensitivity, indecisiveness, constant feelings of being disliked, and/or a subservient attitude to others. The doormat type person—the frightened, fragile, meek individual–may be suffering from deficient Manipura energy. Those who cannot set personal boundaries often need Manipura flow. The system will try to balance unbalanced Manipura with Vishuddha energy of the fifth chakra and vice versa. So, again, there I was, an excessive ego-maniac with a closed off Vishuddha (Throat) Chakra.

Physically, Manipura governs the pancreas, gallbladder, stomach, liver, and sense of sight. Those who need visual proof–to see everything in order to believe it–may benefit from balancing their Manipura energy. Balanced Manipura energy would also be of great help to those who don't believe anything even when they see it—those who can deny what's happening in front of their very eyes–because, remember, Manipura helps us digest and this includes what we consume via our eyes as well as food. Anyone living in fear of themselves or of the world would benefit from balancing this energy center.

Anahata - Heart Chakra

Continuing up to the Heart Center we find the core of our being–the point of balance within–the Anahata Chakra. This is the soul and spiritual center; the doorway to our Higher Nature, the balancing point—the very center of our being. This spinning, green wheel is where body, mind and spirit meet and unite as one, and it is the home to the essence of who we are on a spiritual level...*Love*.

The center of the system, Anahata works alone as the meeting point serving as the bridge between our lower density "human" vibrations to our higher density "spiritual" vibrations. It is the channel for the upward flow of our energy, so, quite fittingly Anahata connects us to the element of Air. This is the place that allows the heavy, dense emotions such as anger, fear, jealousy, and sadness to be uplifted and transformed. This is what allows us to move on, grieve, forgive, and transform.

Anahata energy governs our sense of love, compassion, self-acceptance, emotional balance, spiritual growth, and harmony with others. Balanced Anahata brings open-heartedness, affection, love, compassion, harmonious personality, feelings of genuine well-being, and harmony towards self and others, as well as identification with the true self, and/or feelings of freedom and independence from surroundings. Balance here brings the release of attachments and needs, and the relinquishing of the need for a fixed identity and ego. When Anahata is flowing we see through the illusion of ego. Unconditional love and affection, as well as healthy devotion to sacred things, are signs of balanced and open Anahata.

In an unbalanced system, the excessive or overactive Anahata may manifest as extreme jealousy, inappropriate emotional responses and expressions or lack thereof, and/or no emotional boundaries. Those who "wear their hearts on their sleeves" and just bleed their emotions all over their surroundings may suffer from an overactive Anahata. Someone who puts their emotions on others, taking no emotional responsibility for themselves, may suffer imbalance here. Healthy emotional boundaries require that we take responsibility for our own emotions in order to heal our own shit, and this is something we do via an open Heart Chakra.

That wasn't me if you haven't caught on yet. You could say that I was a bit the opposite of what I just described; rough and tough, if I may. I was emotionally dead to a point where I was almost sociopathic. I suffered from a severe energy block at the heart level which resulted in extremely deficient (if any) Anahata energy. This manifested as ruthlessness, cold-heartedness, bitterness, and a complete inability to feel my emotions. I would think about them, but was unable to connect with an actual emotional feeling. I was cut-off from them, fractured from my emotional body. As my friends used to say, I was like a robot. Feeling rejected early in life as a child unbalanced my Anahata, and we will get into those juicy details later on.

Physically, Anahata governs the thymus, heart, liver, lungs and blood flow, as well as sense of touch. It's not a coincidence I would suffer from some breathing and lung problems for part of my life, is it?

Those who need touch as proof of love may be dancing to the tune of an unbalanced Anahata, as is true for the opposite, those who dislike being touched. Touch is an innate part of why we come to Earth to have a human existence. So if there is a problem surrounding touching or being touched, it may be reflecting an Anahata imbalance. In a balanced system touch may still be preferred and enjoyed as a communication of love, but it is no longer a need that causes problems for us. For example, I no longer need you to touch me all the time to prove that you love me. I see it in other ways too.

Vishuddha - Throat Chakra

Now, my personal favorite! Moving up to the throat, we find the blue center of the Vishuddha Chakra.

The elemental connection here is Ether. This is the place where I had my most severe blockage, which resulted in a fracture from my spiritual body. This is the portal and center of communication, inner truth, creativity, self-expression, sound, intuition, and identity. Balanced Vishuddha energy has no problem speaking up for or hearing the truth. Balanced Vishuddha stands firm and confident in itself and its being, all while maintaining a playfully detached view of self. This is a beautiful truth that I now get to live today.

Balanced Vishuddha creates a desire to live, speak, and hear truths. It governs a sense of diplomacy with others, tact, loving honesty, and purity in relationships. When we connect with the higher truth of the interconnectedness of All that Is, we are mastering Vishuddha energy. Overactive or excessive energy at the Throat Chakra may manifest as willful, controlling, argumentative, and/or judgmental behaviors. Someone who talks excessively or is prone to hurtful speech when they are suffering would benefit from balancing their overactive Vishuddha energy. Often Vishuddha gets thrown off balance in response to underactive Manipura.

I was never allowed to speak up for myself or communicate as a child, so my Vishuddha energy went defunct. As I grew up I found that I couldn't speak my truth even when I wanted to. I was quiet, shy, insecure, introverted, and could not create. I had no faith in anyone or anything. Later, my Manipura would kick into overdrive to balance this, which resulted in my egotistical and obnoxious facade for the world, as well as serving as a catalyst for my addictions.

Vishuddha governs the thyroid, throat, upper lungs, arms, and digestive tract, as well as the sense of hearing. Again, it's no coincidence that most of my physical problems, which I will illustrate in the next chapter, revolved around these organs and senses. Those of you who, like I was once, need to hear everything for yourself to trust it may want to balance Vishuddha energy, as would those who won't hear the truth no matter how bluntly it is spoken.

Poor listeners may suffer blocks here, as well as people who twist everything they hear for their own benefit in order to suit their own version of events. Anyone suffering from poor communication skills will benefit from Vishuddha healing and alignment. And, remember, communication is *listening as well as talking.*

Ajna - Third Eye Chakra

Moving up to the head space, we find the Ajna Chakra, or the Third-Eye, located just behind the center of the forehead between the eyes. It's color is indigo and this wheel of energy connects us to the element of Light. The higher mind connects here; this is the seat of knowing, intuition, altruism, realistic perception, and spiritual sense. Balanced Ajna may display as imagination, knowing, realistic perceptions, clarity, ability to see the world as it is *without emotional and mental filters,* and/or the ability to practice forgiveness and compassion.

The mastery of Ajna energy manifests as self-discipline while maintaining flexibility with a quietness of mind, which allows space for clarity where we can hear the Higher Self. This results in psychic knowing and manifestation abilities. As mentioned earlier, Ajna energy may become unbalanced in an attempt to correct skewed Svadhisthana energy. This can result in the rise of intellectual defenses in response to feelings of fear, which are stemming from deficient or excessive Svadhisthana.

Wow, right? Did you have any idea all this stuff was related? It is!

Overactive or excessive Ajna may manifest as extreme self-centeredness, excessive over-analyzation, and over-intellectualization of everything, and/or constant thoughts of I, me, and mine. Think about the extreme opposite of what spiritual behavior looks like. The constant reeling of the monkey mind and the need to figure it all out arises from excessive energy in the Third Eye. In my personal opinion, the thinking problem and inability to focus for very long, aka monkey mind, in our society stems from this imbalance. In its simplest essence it is a manifestation of too much mind and not enough heart. When Ajna energy is unbalanced, the mind is constantly in overdrive clamoring for the next perceived solution to the problems that it creates all by itself.

My Svadhisthana was very deficient, so my Ajna kicked into overdrive. I lived in analytical and noisy chaos of the mind for many years, and I kept it all inside.

It nearly killed me.

This exhausted me by the age of 16, which is where my love of opiates would fit in later. (Gory details coming soon!)

Underactive Ajna may present as delusion, unclear thoughts, rigidity, inability to think for oneself, and/or relying on attachments to beliefs and identities. Behaviors like this fit well with the manipulative behavior of my underactive Svadhisthana, paving the way for me to believe my own delusions.

Physically, Ajna governs the pituitary gland, spine, lower brain, left eye, nose, and ears. Ajna also governs the "sixth sense" of deep and intuitive knowing. Those who dismiss everything they can't explain away may suffer from an unbalanced Ajna Chakra, as might those who are so caught up in the higher realms, their feet are barely on the ground. It doesn't pay to love in the clouds just like it doesn't serve us to live mired in dense negative emotions. It's all about balance.

Sahasrara - Crown Chakra

Last, but certainly not least, we come to the top of the head where the Sahasrara, or Crown, Chakra is found. It is just at the crown of the head, the spot that is still soft during our first days born to Earth. Its color is violet, almost white—picture light and purity. The elemental correspondence of Sahasrara is that of the Spirit; this is the center of higher consciousness. We find the unification of all colors and all elements of the self here—body, mind, and spirit are one. The unification of All That Is and the realization of this connection is governed here. This is the center of divine bliss, wisdom, self-realization, and connection to the Higher Self.

Balanced Sahasrara energy will be unbiased, unprejudiced, awake, and aware. Enlightened. Someone who lives in a higher plane of consciousness has well-functioning and flowing Sahasrara energy. In response to unbalanced Muladhara (Root) energy Sahasrara will over or under-compensate. The excessive or overactive energy may manifest as egocentricity, and/or an incessant need to intellectualize everything. The extreme example of excessive Sahasrara would be the sociopath (which I thought I was once) or the charismatic cult leader. The unbalanced, ego-centric Sahasrara tries to compensate for the deficient Muladhara, which constantly feels unsafe and threatened all the time.

On the other side, the deficient or underactive Sahasrara may show up as someone who has no spiritual aspirations of higher living, no inspiration, no consideration of anything more than what we get on the physical plane, and/or who is extremely rigid in their thinking and ways of living, such as very black and white thinkers who can't see the grey area that always exists.

The mastery of Sahasrara energy results in balance and integration of the lower three chakras, along with their own personal qualities, into a fluid and functional system. It also brings about a space of living in the awareness that we are indeed spiritual beings living a human existence rather than just animated physical bodies struggling to survive this earthly experience. The realization of self as part of the greater Collective Consciousness is very connected to Sahasrara energy. This is what we know as self-realization in the path of Kriya Yoga which I will discuss in more depth later.

Physically, Sahasrara governs the pineal gland, which even science now acknowledges as the spiritual center, as well as the higher brain and right eye. (Side note on the pineal gland: do some research and start digging. Start with the ancient Sumerians and pine cone symbolism. Follow it to why there is a massive tribute to a pine cone even in the Vatican.)

Unbalanced Sahasrara may show up as someone who can't or won't consider anything beyond the material/physical realm in front of them. The ego-maniac who doesn't care whom he/she hurts in the process of getting whatever it is he or she wants may very likely be a combination of overactive Sahasrara trying to balance underactive Muladhara like I was. On the other hand, someone who is so consumed and blinded by greed and material possessions, and is so convinced these possessions are survival needs they can't see past the material plane, may be suffering from the opposite: an underactive Sahasrara and overactive Muladhara.

Thus we have seven major chakras, with our beautiful and loving Anahata at the center balancing it all and reminding us of our true essence. Physically, our hearts do the most work as well as energetically. The heart is a powerful organ, much more powerful than they tell us in high school anatomy. This is another place I would suggest further exploring on your own the electromagnetic power and field of the heart center and its ability to shift vibration.

Muladhara and Sahasrara are a team. Svadhisthana and Ajna work together, as do Manipura and Vishuddha. That being said, the whole system also works together to deliver unity and balance within us. When we become self-aware, finding the place of honesty with ourselves, we begin to see our behaviors and patterns in a drastic new light. We begin to see them as something we have a lot of control over rather than something we are a victim of. Here is where we can see how we fit into this system and where we personally suffer imbalances, blocks, or fractures.

I'd like to share that it's only in hindsight that I can see and write about what I now know and choose to give to you in this book. At the time when I was living the blocks and their manifestations, I didn't know any of this. I certainly couldn't *see* any of it. I wouldn't hear any of it, and I wouldn't believe the mumbo jumbo if anyone had tried to tell me back then. This close-minded and negative thinking was all related to my own blocks and imbalances, of which I will share all the gory details. I am not a prisoner of these issues any longer; I have found freedom. Now I *know* better, so I *do* better for myself which allows me to do better for the world.

I have a happy, healthy, and balanced life of contentment. Keeping the system balanced and flowing is a daily practice, but one that is well worth my time and energy, as it has me feeling physically well, whole, complete, happy, satisfied, trusting, open, safe, and content. This is so much more than any horrible pharmaceutical or street drug would be doing for me, and, having tried everything under the sun to quiet my mind and give me peace, I now know there is no substance out there which would bless me with the serenity and balance I feel today through energy work and connection.

It's such a simple solution in such a complicated world. If you're reading this book, I'm sure you've heard at least once in life that our physical symptoms of illness are the sign of deeper problems. I know I had heard it before I came to understand it, but always dismissed it as *"pfffft, whatever."* Remember, I had no comprehension of myself past the physical body, so why would that statement even cause me to bat an eye? It wouldn't and it didn't. Until it did and that's when I woke up. In hindsight, I understand some things and see so clearly. Hindsight is 20/20 right? Hits home for me today.

So now, beautiful soul, if you've picked up this book and made it this far, you must believe a little bit of what I am saying about how our spiritual, emotional, and mental issues manifest as physical ailments. Or maybe you're just reading it so you can solidify the belief that I am nuts. Either way, it's okay—I hope I satisfy. That being said I would now like to share a little bit about my personal adventures with the physical manifestations of my unbalanced and blocked chakra system as they presented themselves to me.

He who knows others is learned;
He who knows himself is wise.
~Lao-tzu, Tao te Ching

Chapter 2
My Unbalanced Body

A healthy outside starts from the inside. ~Robert Urich

Physical ailments suffered throughout a lifetime illustrate exactly how interconnected the body, mind, and spirit are. The physical symptoms of illness and dis-ease that we see manifesting in our bodies are just symptoms of something deeper. They are linked to our emotional/mental/spiritual blocks and energetic imbalances.

If you want more evidence and in depth explanation of this, I suggest Louise Hay. For me, personally, my physical symptoms came in the form of ear, nose, throat, neck, and shoulder problems and injuries, as well as a particular form of cancer. After briefly hearing about my particular chakra blocks, it's ironic enough, isn't it? Having shared a bit about my personal story already, I will now dive deeper with you to show you just how related my physical ailments were to my imbalances.

I'll never forget the day I was diagnosed with cancer. Hodgkin's Lymphoma to be exact. I was 25 years old, and it was the very beginning of December. I already knew my diagnosis was coming back positive, as deep down inside something was whispering to me. Intuitively, I knew, but I'd spent the last two months since I found the lump in my neck denying what I inherently knew. I was really good at denial by that point of my life. I could tell myself anything, and, if it didn't suit me, I just denied it. And I believed whatever I was telling myself...that's the scary part.

It worked for me with problems, emotions, events, and even people. Just pretend it doesn't exist and it will go away right? That was my motto. Of course this wasn't at the forefront of my conscious mind like it is now. I wasn't aware of it back then, it was just my *modus operandi* for a long time. This insight merely comes from hindsight and the clarity of vision I now practice through my energy and chakra healing work. I know, I know...this is one of those "If I knew then what I know now" moments. Back then I was an avoider and I was overwhelmed by life and its trials and tribulations. I remember distinctly thinking that I had already suffered enough as a drug addict, hadn't I? I couldn't have cancer on top of that. I didn't know how to deal with anything, so I just avoided it.

The funniest thing is *that's why I ended up with cancer in the first place.* Because I was an avoider, a denier, a stuffer of my anger and bitterness. So there I was at age 25 with a cancer of the lymphatic system. Lymph filters out all the junk from the organs and cells. All of the waste. So my body, ironically, developed a dis-ease of mutinous, out of control cell growth, aka cancer, within the very system meant to cleanse and purge the waste of cellular life. If that wasn't a screaming red flag from my body saying, *"Clean me out! HELP!"* I don't know what is. But, me, being the champion denier of all things not suited to me, clearly wasn't acknowledging anything at this point in my life, so how could I let go of what no longer served me if I couldn't even acknowledge its existence?

I couldn't clean anything out because I wouldn't admit it was there. I can't clean a mess I can't see, can I?!? This inability to filter my emotions, thoughts, identities, and everything else was a direct manifestation of my very clouded, unbalanced, and blocked up chakra system. There are so many issues I just highlighted which point to various chakra imbalances, and they physically manifested in the form of cancer for me.

Coincidence? I think not. Just like my lymphatic system couldn't flow and do its job filtering out the waste from my organs, my chakra system couldn't do its job of filtering my low density energies upwards to mesh with and be balanced by my higher vibrational energies. Thus, my body was a giant, cloudy, blocked up system of ick. Picture a stagnant pool of murky water just sitting there, and you'll have a lovely vision of what my energetic body was looking like.

Again, I'll say that in hindsight, I see all this as clear as day, but at the time I was not aware in the slightest.

Honestly, I didn't really even understand what cancer was until years after mine showed up. I was so caught in avoidance that I took my diagnosis, didn't bother to learn anything, and just shoved it down within me adding it to the various other traumas I had been stuffing and cementing over for all of my life.

I was at age 25 when I found a lump and ignored it for two months even though my intuition was screaming at me. Then I started having trouble breathing. I finally had a biopsy and then took my diagnosis with my head down and two tears. I shuffled through chemo and radiation on complete autopilot. In all of my hard-headed stubbornness, I certainly wasn't going to admit fear or defeat.

Did I mention yet that I'm a Taurus to boot? If you're into astrology then you know why I'm telling you this. I was like a robot—I just handled it like I handled life, cold and collected on the outside and pissed the fuck off on the inside. I had no ability to process any of this at the time due to my defunct and very unbalanced chakra system and a complete fracture of my body, mind, and spirit. I was well and truly fractured from my emotional body by this time, which, of course, I will be sharing in all its glory later on.

Looking back on that day, I guess I was probably in shock. Like I said, I knew deep down, from the moment I found the lump and started having trouble breathing, that I was sick. But I couldn't and wouldn't accept that. Cancer was for the weak, and I didn't have time for that. I had a really poor opinion of anything I saw as weak. So hearing it come out of my doctor's mouth that day was a little bit surreal. I still couldn't really accept it as he was saying it. I remember his asking me if I was okay and if he could call someone for me, because, naturally, being who I was, I went to the appointment alone. That's how I operated for most of my life. Solo. I had people in my life, such as family, friends, and relationships, but they were always kept at arm's length outside the walls, on my say so.

So there I was, alone and sitting in the office of the man who had been my ear, nose, and throat doctor and surgeon for 25 years (I'll get to those issues too), staring at him as he told me my positive cancer diagnoses. I vaguely recall having a brief desire to punch him, as though *"How dare you tell me I have cancer? You lie!"* Then I just remember telling myself *"No. Whatever."* This was followed by *"Well, this fucking sucks. Go figure. Can I catch a fucking break? First I'm a drug addict, now I have cancer. I really am cursed. Can a girl catch a friggin break in life? There's a book to be written in all this...."* And I almost laughed. I wouldn't accept this diagnosis. I remember a whole lot of inner dialogue consisting of quite a few repetitions of "Fuck this." Yep, that was me in all my glory. If I didn't like it my response was *"Fuck you and fuck this."*

"I will not accept a death sentence, and I will not be scared. Fear is for the weak!" my mind cried. I see now that I was very scared, but I was so detached from my emotional body that I was able to deny having feelings of fear about my diagnosis and actually believe myself. Now my ability to delude myself is almost funny, but back then it was a serious situation. I was angry, but I wasn't going to

show that. I wanted to cry. However, I wouldn't be allowing myself that indulgence either.

Before we talk about the hell that is cancer I want to say this–the irony of the whole thing is that I've had throat and ear problems my entire life. Allow me to take you back to the beginning. Before my first birthday, I had tubes placed in my ears to properly line up my eardrums and canals, so they could properly drain and do their part in my sinus system.

If you don't know, tubes are tiny, T-shaped plastic tubes that line up the ear canal and eardrum. If not properly lined up, the ears don't drain, they clog, frequent ear infections happen, and life is miserable for the child, as it was for me. Ear infections are excruciating. This is something that I eventually grew out of and my last pair of tubes were out of my ears at 14, but it was something that severely affected my social anxiety and sense of being 'normal' as a child. I felt like a freak having to wear earplugs when we would go swimming. *"Why me?"* I would moan in my head. I was angry even then. I resented being different, and I resented the fact that I was afraid every time I had surgery but couldn't actually express that.

Even back to my earliest memories, I could not express my emotions. I remember stubbornly refusing to cry as they would put the oxygen mask on me even though I was so frightened. I was emotionally incapacitated from the start, vain and insecure, and so afraid of being weak thanks to that underactive Manipura energy.

As I grew older and my Throat Chakra grew more blocked, ear infections continued to plague me, as well as sinus infections and colds. My hearing sucked when my ears weren't draining properly. I was prone to sinus issues and nasty coughs that would linger for weeks, along with what felt like constant stuffy, snotty noses. I was the picture of a snotty, little, dirty child, as I didn't like showers for a few years there either.

Ironically enough, from a very early age, my ability to vocally communicate my needs was practically nonexistent. I couldn't speak up for myself without this overwhelming urge of feeling like a stupid, needy, foolish little shit. Don't get me wrong, I was *physically* capable of talking; I just wouldn't do it. I wanted to, but it was as though there was an invisible gag over me that wouldn't allow it. My parents love to tell stories of me as a baby in my crib where I would wake up and want out, but instead of crying or screaming like most babies would do, I would instead stand up in my crib and hold on to the bars, shaking the crib until someone came and got me. Frustration at its finest I guess. Obviously my blocked Vishuddha energy flow happened quite early on, and was manifesting in my physical problems from the start.

Something to note is that we can be born with blocked and unbalanced systems. Just like we grow physically in the womb, we also grow energetically and emotionally. Depending on our mother's surroundings while we were in utero, on the state of affairs between both parents, as well as both of their own states of balance or lack thereof, we can develop imbalances before we are even born. Everything else is passed to us, so why not energetic problems too? This sure makes sense to me, since, from my earliest recollection, neither one of my parents possessed any healthy measure of communication or self-expression that I was able to see. Being as empathic as I am, I'm pretty sure part of what I came into the world carrying was passed on from them.

I have clear memories of being so consumed with my anger as a small child that I felt as though it was going to drown me, while having no proper outlet for it. I was born an emotional firestorm and highly empathic, which we will talk more about as we get into the emotional/mental body.

My earliest and strongest memories are of my emotions, yet the story of much of my life consists of denying this massive part of myself, which resulted in massive dis-ease for me. I denied my emotional body to the point that I was convinced that it no longer even existed within me. I believe my emotional issues, physical illnesses, dis-ease, and inability to express myself were all directly linked to my energetic blocks and fractures. Because, now, these problems don't exist for me. But we will get to that.

At some point in my 20s, I remember reading something astrology related. I believe it was a book on a combination of Western and Chinese zodiac. The section applicable to me combined all of this Taurus information with my Chinese zodiac, which was Year of the Goat. In that book I learned that not only was I energetically fucked from the start, I was also born under the most bullheaded stubborn and obstinate star sign combination there could be. You can say I had my work cut out for me, and still do.

Anyways, this horoscope got way into details about characteristics, personality traits, physical problems, and all sorts of stuff. I clearly remember reading that I would be prone to neck, throat, and ear problems in my life. I remember my awe that this book was telling me something so right on about me. Knowing what I know now, I wish it had been followed up with a nice section on chakras and meditation so I could've understood then what I do now and possibly balanced myself a lot sooner. It would have prevented a ton of drama in my life, but that just wasn't my path and I accept that. I have to accept it because I refuse to live a life of regrets, victimhood, and what-ifs.

Knowing all of this is where I find the irony. Like I said, I was born under a sun sign in an astrological year that set me up to be prone to throat problems, and those problems sure manifested without my knowing why. Who knew everything was energy back then? I sure didn't. I became aware of my inability to communicate quite early on, *decades* before I came across the information on my chakras and how to heal them. I just had no idea what it was linked to or what I could do about it. I thought it was all just an inherent aspect of my makeup; a fixed element of my personality. I told myself I was alright, and that I just didn't *want* to talk so much.

Funny enough, the first book on this very subject of chakras found me shortly after I became truly aware of my inability to communicate and function as I saw others doing. Just after I admitted I had a serious problem connection within myself and decided I wanted to do something about it, a book crossed my path. It brought up and awoke within me a fierce determination to address this problem because, by this point of my life, I was thoroughly convinced that my inability to communicate was one of the driving forces that kept me locked in a cycle of destroying my life. Clearly, as I came to understand, it had also been manifesting as severe dis-ease and illness in my physical body. By this point in time I had had enough of feeling like a pile of shit physically at the ripe age of 30. I was tired. I was beat up, and I wanted change. Change sure did find me.

But first, in order for all that wisdom and change to find me, some things had to happen to give me a sharp kick to the ass known as a wake-up call. Or, in my case, wake-up call*s*. So first, I got cancer. And, like I shared with you, I was pissed. Going back to that day, all I could think of on my drive home was "*My hair is going to fall out, and I am going to be ugly.*" Then the denier voice, forever masquerading as the optimist, would say "*Maybe it won't. You'll be alright.*" Yep, I've got cancer and I'm worried about *my hair*. Not dying…but my appearance. Priorities. What can I say? I was still as vain as they come during that time. Vanity is a manifestation of insecurity and egotistical thinking which are all related to the energetic imbalances found within the chakras. I was more unbalanced, blocked, and vain than ever before.

I approached cancer like someone held at gunpoint to do a job they hated. I'm good like that. When something nasty needs doing I can shut down and just handle the business. That's what happens when there is a fracture between the mind, body, and spirit—life is mechanical, even at its most frightening. It's almost robotic in the face of things that make most people cringe. Even in the most scary times; not even then can you get in touch with the emotions. Your own life is playing out as though you are watching someone else's on screen and feeling no emotional response to it. I always thought I would be a good medic for a war zone because I was that robotic and non-emotional person for years. And the worst part is that I thought it was *normal*. I could step over dead bodies to handle my business, no emotions attached, ever. And no, I didn't want to talk about it. Just leave me alone thank you very much. Nor did I see it as any type of problem. I thought I was just strong for being this way.

So when it came to cancer, I showed up, shut up, and handled it. I muscled through chemotherapy sessions and went to work bartending afterwards in order to keep my health insurance. I felt like shit. I was exhausted. I wanted to crawl in a hole and cry. But I wasn't going to tell anyone this. I was afraid if I didn't work, I wouldn't have health insurance, so I muscled through it and showed up. My hair was falling out. I was losing weight. I was miserable. And I wanted to cry every single time I sat in that goddamned chemo chair, and they hooked me up to the poison drip. I cried myself to sleep at night as I pulled out clumps of my hair. I couldn't tell anyone how miserable I was. I'm not even sure I *wanted* to tell anyone. Not my friends, not my boyfriend, not my mom. I just didn't even think about it. It was a very numb time. There was no thought process about it at the time. I just went about my business and my life. I was so fractured I truly thought I was fine. I couldn't even feel the disconnect. My doctor suggested a support group. Yeah right. As if I was going to do that.

My whole chakra system was unbalanced and suffering, and the blocks were growing worse every day. I was choked off, and my energy flow was absolutely stagnated. My heart couldn't connect with my body; I was just numb. My Higher Self was floating around up there trying to reach out, but couldn't get through the concrete barriers around my throat area in my Vishuddha chakra. Even if I wanted to cry out and tell someone I was dying and afraid inside, I don't know that I actually could have. I was so cut off from my emotional body I really thought and believed that I didn't actually have emotions. Seriously. It was like there were three separate entities and versions of myself that couldn't communicate with one another.

I weighed out for a while if I was a sociopath. "Maybe I am," I thought. But *"Fuck it"* I said, because to me this just meant I didn't have to care about anyone or anything. Not caring was way easier than caring. Or so it seemed to me back then.

I tried to care, and I just couldn't find it in me anymore. I'd picked up a belief somewhere along the way that said it was easier not to care, and that would be the motto of my life right up until it almost killed me. I spent 34 years trying to show the world just how much I didn't care and how I didn't need anyone or anything in it, all while carrying the weight of the world on my shoulders. More irony, I know. I saw everything and felt everything happening to me and around me, but those feelings couldn't get through to my intellect so they just festered in my lower chakra system wreaking havoc on my body. Unbeknownst to me, I carried on living in my world of intellect and reason with my blocked off Throat Chakra, priding myself on having no feelings and being strong.

Naturally, the next to manifest was my neck and shoulder problems, which showed up in the form of injuries. I've come to learn that the body will try to get our attention by whatever means necessary: herniated discs, stiffness, and pain, combined with chronic sinus and throat problems and bronchitis, which would turn into full-fledged cases of laryngitis at least once a month. It was the ongoing joke at work how I lost my voice again because I yelled too much. Because inherently, I was so frustrated at my inability to communicate, that when I actually would speak I was loud to make up for not being able to express the important stuff. I had no idea how to communicate, yet I thought I didn't want to. I fed myself lies about how I didn't want people in my life and I was happy being closed off and alone. It's quite amazing how a blockage at the level of communication can seriously isolate us from the world around us, even when we are surrounded by people. Funny how that works isn't it?

So, there I was by the ripe old age of 25, feeling–physically–like I had lived three lifetimes already. I felt old and beat up at 25! Juggling the weight of my very disconnected three separate entities (body, mind, spirit) was hard. I was living three lives at the same time.

My body was sick; my mind relentless; and my soul was drowning in a deep prison of anger and darkness. I'd had numerous surgeries, biopsies, sicknesses, laryngitis, neck injuries, cancer, chemo, radiation, drug addiction, shoulder and back problems. I was tense as a bow string, and yet I was continuing to waltz around as though "I'm fine." Slap on a smile and give a nod, and go to work. I'm good, let's do this. Make a joke, poke some fun—let's go. I was like a pressure cooker waiting to just blow up. This is why, in hindsight, there's no surprise when the cancer showed up. It was my body's way of screaming for me to wake up and clean house. To let go of all the toxic energies I'd been carrying around since birth. Only they don't teach us that in school, so who knew?

It's no wonder that ten years later–around the age of 34–by the time I learned about chakras, I was so wound up I was ready to explode. I'm really surprised that I'm actually alive, honestly. I vacillated between wanting to die, wanting to kill someone, and wanting to blow something up. I loathed the world and its people, including myself. Especially myself! (I didn't know yet that the outer world was just reflecting my inner state, and I was a victim all the way. But we'll get to that.)

I believe now if I hadn't found drugs back when I did, I would have probably killed someone by that point in life. Or perhaps myself. Back then, I certainly never would have believed anyone who tried to tell me I could feel as good physically as I do now just by taking time to care for and time to balance myself. I would've had some nasty response for them surrounding how they had no idea what it was like to have lived my life. I cringe a little writing that because people stuck in that mindset are so challenging to help…and I was one of them for so long.

"Health is a relationship between you and your body"
~Terri Guillemets

Fractured

Chapter 3
Balancing the Chakras/Physical Body

"To keep the body in good health is a duty, otherwise we shall not be able to keep our mind strong and clear."
~Buddha

All this talk about imbalance and blocks, cancer and anger, darkness and struggle. Let's get light for a moment before we get really dark, shall we? This is the best part! There is hope for the most mangled among us. There is hope for the tired, dis-eased, ill, weak, frail, beat up, sad, and angry among us.

That's the beautiful thing about the human body and the chakra system—they are both so resilient and miraculous! When taken care of they both respond quickly and beautifully. The body is our temple—the only home we have for this existence on Earth. We may be spiritual beings but, in this earthly dimension and reality, we need our dense human forms to have the full human experience, so let's take care of our homes. Without the body we miss out on the physical delights and lessons that we came to Earth to learn.

Obviously, I haven't always lived by this credo, but I do now, and my physical health is amazing. It's never been better! It's truly nothing short of miraculous. I'm not going to lie, I have a few problems and lingering injuries from the years of living as though I wanted to die– pushing myself to extremes of body and mind, abusing my body as though I had another back-up–but, nonetheless and despite these, I've never felt better. I feel alive, vibrant, clear, and accepting of my body in whatever shape it's in.

I no longer feel a need to punish myself with unhealthy eating habits, anorexia, chemicals, drugs, alcohol, cigarettes, or any other impurities I can get into my body. I no longer need to medicate every unpleasant physical sensation and feeling with some pharmaceutically created medication under the guise that all unpleasant feelings must be eradicated. That is a major myth of the mind that I no longer carry the belief that any feelings are bad. I now just see them as they are…feelings. Good, bad or indifferent, they are simply what I make them, and they are nothing more than vibrations of energy that move through us in the same way that clouds move across the sky.

Since my awakening and day of reconnection, I stopped eating meat, dairy, and sugar, and gave up cigarettes all around the same time. It was a natural evolution of the alignment and reconnection of body, mind, and spirit within me. And it wasn't an issue for me to do so. I just stopped, as though being guided by a force greater than myself. I don't say this to brag, I say this to illustrate the miraculous occurrences that have taken place as a result of my work to reconnect and balance my body, mind, and spirit through yoga and meditation practice.

When I was 34, I made a commitment to balancing my system and keeping it balanced. I made a decision that I wanted to live and stop merely existing and, since then, I've committed to a path that keeps me aligned and connected. I firmly believe my ability to stop engaging in toxic eating habits, addictions, compulsions, behaviors, and cigarette smoking is a direct physical manifestation of a balanced and healthy chakra system. It's all related to energy flow.

I was one of the most addictive people I've ever known, yet I walked away from things I used to live on because I no longer felt they were energetically and physically good for me. If you don't know me, that's a miracle in itself. I believe that upon cleaning, healing, and balancing the system on an energetic level, we become more sensitive to unhealthy energies and behaviors which clog up and pollute us. Thus, all of a sudden, it becomes simple to cut them out. All of a sudden we notice that the need and desire for toxic things has left us.

When we break free from just feeling okay and average and reach our highest physical potential, we no longer want to poison our systems with junk. When we are connected, we start truly living and we find that the need for outside "things" as a distraction or medication fade away. At this point, we also begin to understand that many of our physical limitations are often self-imposed because we allow our mind to be lazy and make excuses. The mind doesn't want to work to surpass its own beliefs which are familiar and comfortable, so we make excuses about why we can't physically do things that we don't want to do.

"Your words control your life, your progress, your results, even your mental and physical health. You cannot talk like a failure and expect to be successful." ~Germany Kent

Physical Balance

Now let's discuss *how* to balance the system.

First of all—healing. Like any old festering, infected wound, we must first cleanse the contamination. We must do the same for our chakras. We must shine light into our chakra system to see what's actually going on in there. We don't know until we look. We have to shine that light into the deepest corners of our being into all those places we want to keep boarded up. The best way to do this is through yoga and meditation. These practices are so healing for all the bodies, but especially the physical body. When we can leave the mind, this brings our awareness to the physical body and suddenly we find we are present in the moment…and that it's quite a lovely place.

We must sit and observe, perhaps for the first time ever, our own chakra system. Shine the light in there and say hello. (See the meditation guide.) There are some great guided healing meditations out there online and in books—I have designed my own personalized for me, and I guide people on their personal journeys by designing personalized chakra meditations for them. I'm not the meditation police, so I suggest any practice that works for you and feels right for your needs. Start with a breathing practice and work through to a cleansing practice.

Again, I offer some in this book, you can research online, or take local classes. I believe any form of meditation works and is beneficial, so I don't suggest anything you are not comfortable with. Mediation is not an identity. Allow yourself space to try different schools of practice. Look into pranayama, Buddhist, Zen, Vipassana, visualization, mantras, affirmations, yantras, chanting, Solfeggio, or anything else that shows up in your life. It's showing up for a reason.

Diet - You are what you eat!

People ask me all the time why I no longer eat dairy, meat, or anything from animals. I answer by explaining how I disagree with the treatment of the animals, as they are kept in inhumane and uncompassionate ways. I believe that animals have feelings and they are forced to live in fear and pain. As a result, when consuming meat, it's so much more than meat. It's toxins, hormones, and bad energy. That's when many people look at me like I'm nuts. Why ask questions if they don't want the answer? But seriously, I urge you to think about what you're actually consuming along with your food.

I believe when we consume the meat of animals who have been forced to live in energies of pain, anger, and fear that we are then consuming those energies as well. I noticed that I became very sensitive to this after cleansing and healing myself when I could no longer bring myself to eat meat without feeling sick.

The compassionate reasoning that had awoken by unblocking my Anahata chakra started to shift my eating habits and my energy work carries it through as a sustainable choice. Once we have cleansed and healed ourselves and we feel the possibility that exists for us, we stop wanting to keep pumping crap into our systems. It's a natural result of healing. We become more and more mindful of what we consume. We must or we will end up back in the bowels of heavy dense energies once again. If we keep up a daily practice, our good feelings maintain themselves.

Please keep in mind, this does not have to be an all or nothing task, nor does it have to be a massive undertaking or life overhaul. We can start where we are and just take one step to begin to eat more mindfully by doing the following:

- Pay attention to what you eat and how much.
- Begin to make a shift from processed to more organic.
- Go slowly and be gentle with yourself.
- Cut out meat where you can.
- Opt for hormone-free, organic, non-GMO whenever possible.
- Start limiting sugar and caffeine.

The best thing we can do for ourselves is to simply start practicing mindfulness. Wherever you are, make a beginning. There's never so perfect a time as right now.

Bring to your own awareness what your diet looks like and what changes you feel need to be made. You'll know what you need if you can get past the chatter of the mind to hear it. Once you have worked through some energy and chakra balancing, it will be easier than your mind may be telling you it will be right now as you read this. Just remember to breathe. The first thing to remember when considering powerful changes and action in your life is not to get overwhelmed. You don't have to change everything at once.

We did not get unbalanced and blocked in one day, so we must be patient and loving with ourselves. It takes time. If we consume food with the belief that it's energy and fuel, it may help us to be more concerned with what type of fuel we put in.

Do you want to put crap gasoline into your super sweet Maserati sports car? No. So this is where you stop putting it in your body. Of course, though, if we feel lousy about ourselves then we won't care what fuel we are putting in, so we must have a tune up; we must wake up our self-love and self-respect.

The relationship with food is a direct reflection of the relationship with the self. So we must balance and clear body, mind, and soul for an overall lasting effect on our well-being to take effect. It's time for some TLC for your body. Are you ready?

Chakra balancing.
There are so many ways to help cleanse, heal, and balance chakras. We can do yoga—which I cover more in

the section on mind because, as much as it seems physical and carries immense physical benefits, to me, yoga is very much mind game. The asanas are designed to help cleanse and heal our physical bodies as well as our chakras; they prepare the physical body and mind for meditation.

A fantastic place to start is affirmations. When I started I had no idea what I was doing or how to quiet my mind and start believing in my worth, so I practiced affirmations daily. They kept my mind busy and rewrote some of my erroneous and self-limiting beliefs that were stored deep in my body. We can use affirmations for balancing each particular chakra. Here are some examples of my personal affirmations/mantras:

Muladhara - *I am. I am safe. I am alive. I am one with the Earth. I draw my strength from the Earth. I am grounded in the present. I smell the Earth and it cleanses me. I allow the Earth to heal and balance me.*
Svadhisthana - *I feel. I am creative. I am fluid and I am flexible. My emotions may flow like water and it is okay. They may come they may go, I am constant and I'm not my emotions. I taste the water of life and I am cleansed. It is safe to let go. I can trust.*
Manipura - *I do. I am strong. Like the fire of the sun, I am healed. I give what no longer serves me to the fire. I am the light of the sun, and I see the beauty in me. I am here. I am secure. I am worthy and safe. I can compromise.*
Anahata - *I love. I am loved. I am open and I am loving. I forgive myself and others. It is safe to greet the world with love. My heart remains open to the world. I feel the air on*

my face and I can go lightly like air. I can be vulnerable, and it's okay. I am worthy of love. I am balanced and loving. I will love myself and other unconditionally. It starts with me.

Vishuddha - *I speak. I am expressive. Like the wind, I am free and clear. It is safe to express myself and my needs. I am safe in my identity. I can speak and I can listen with love. I am a spiritual being and my spirit expresses itself here. It is safe to communicate. My voice is clear. I can speak my truth with love.*

Ajna - *I see. I am connected. I am calm, peaceful, and centered. I am exactly where I need to be. I am serene, content, and in tune with my higher self. It is safe for my mind to rest and my spirit to soar. I am not my thoughts. My mind is my friend but I am it's master. I can listen to my intuition.*

Sahasrara - *I understand. I am divine. I am the light. I am the healing. I am balanced in body, mind, and spirit. I am you and you are me. We are One. All is as it should be. I am exactly as I am meant to be. I am Divine, whole, and perfect in my existence. I am one with my Higher Self. I can trust my intuition.*

These are helpful because they begin to rewire our thinking patterns about which we will talk more in the mind/emotion chapter. In combination with meditation they can work wonders for shifting our perspective of the world. When we rewire our beliefs big miracles occur. We become conscious creators of reality.

Which brings us to the fascinating realm of the mind, the driver that is so often our jailer and own worst enemy.

Mine was.

Section 2
The Mental/Emotional Body

Fractured

Chapter 4
The Mental Mind

"The mind is everything. What you think you become."
~Buddha

This section is dedicated to discussing the human mind and its basic components, as well as our emotions. I want to share my experience of what it looks like for a mind to be working in an unbalanced, fractured, or blocked system compared to what a mind in a balanced and open system looks like.

The human mind can be a very frightening place. At least I know mine can be, and judging from the atrocities we see on a daily basis, it's easy to assume that anyone's mind has the potential to be dark. I know we like to deny that very real potential, but we will never get well while denying anything. It's powerful in there.

The mind can be our best friend or our worst enemy, depending on our state of balance and discipline. Now that I work to maintain a state of balance within, my mind is my friend and I am its master, rather than the other way around, as it was for many years. That wasn't always the case, as we will discuss very soon. To quickly clarify, when I say 'mind,' I don't necessarily mean the human brain in its physical form. By mind, I mean all of the thought processes, beliefs, patterns of thinking, emotions, programming, conscious, and subconscious that we all possess within.

The mind is a deep, infinite place, and, no matter how deeply we explore it, there's still so much we don't know. I've been diving into the depths of understanding my own mind and its processes for some time now, and there is more to be revealed on a daily basis. Just when I think I know...

Science still doesn't even fully understand the inner working of the human mind. So much of the capacity is left unused, untapped, and wasted. What are we really capable of if we tapped into the full capacity of the human mind? I can only imagine! For example, what if I told you that, rather than being abnormal and freakish, psychic powers are actually normal and every one of us has psychic potential? I believe it to be true. The mind is like a muscle; it must be worked and kept sharp. When cleared of energetic blockage it operates at a higher capacity, which often manifests as "psychic" powers and deeper knowing and understanding. These powers are really just energetic connections with the Higher Self which display as intuition and knowing.

In my experience, once the mind is clear of blockages, toxins, chemicals, and chaotic energetic frequencies which slow it down and dull the reflexes, our mental capacity often rebounds quite fast. Through practice, the mind returns to its natural ability to see, hear, and feel what is not physically obvious. It becomes more attuned to the subtle nuances on the energetic level. It picks up on the unspoken. It begins to see through the delusions we create with the ego in order to help us feel safe in the scattered and chaotic world we live in.

I could get really conspiracy theory here, but I will leave it alone so as not to scare you off. I'll save that for another book or a Facebook Live! If your interest is piqued by that statement, do some research on effects of fluoride on the human mind, what happened to 432 Hz, alpha and theta waves used in TV and advertising, the pineal gland and the Sumerians. Form your own opinions. And please, email me anytime about what you find!

Back to the mind!

For the purposes of the discussion in this book this is the best definition I would like to offer you:

Mind - (Noun) The element of a person that enables them to be aware of the world and their experiences, to think, and to feel; the faculty of consciousness and thought. A particular way of thinking, influenced by a person's profession or environment.

Emotions - (Noun) from Latin meaning disturbance. For my purposes, I would like you to imagine that emotions come from the place where mind and body meet. When we emote something, it *oozes* out of us. Emotions are a physical/energetic response to our thoughts which arise in response to what is occurring around us. Left unchecked, emotions will just ooze all over us and everyone around us.

It's like this: Something occurs in front of us, then the mind creates a thought about said occurrence, and the body/mind then responds to the thought with an emotion. The thought may be "I suck. I am not good enough." Thus, the feeling of rejection arises in the body, which may spur any number of other emotions, such as shame, anger, or sadness.

Walk with me here for a moment. We have a thought, sometimes out of what seems like nowhere. We respond to the thought physically/mentally with an emotion and then react to the emotion based on our programmed belief about that particular emotion. Sound familiar? The *reaction* is where the mess spills out–or emotes–all over the place causing the problems in reaction to the emotion, or the disturbance, as we defined it earlier. We yell; we snap; we cry; we attack verbally or physically; we shut down; we reply with sarcasm (my favorite) or passive aggressiveness; we fall into self-pity or victimhood; we run away; we fight; or we stonewall. The list goes on and on. It never crosses our mind to pause in the moment before reaction because we aren't programmed to realize we *can* pause.

When our chakras are unbalanced and we have stored blocks and traumas, we react from a place of fear and ego like children. This occurs because we don't realize that we don't actually have to *do* anything. We don't know we have a choice. The powerful emotional energy is like a storm raging within us, and we fall prey to its reactive wrath. We falsely believe everything needs a reaction from us. We think we are responding, but we aren't. *We are reacting.* Responses are thought out. Reactions are fueled by the moment and by pre-programmed beliefs and defense mechanisms.

When left unchecked, unbalanced, and unhealed, it's all a bit of a big mess of thoughts and emotions feeding off of one another and based on beliefs which aren't even logical. It's a vicious cycle of repetitive and destructive thinking when left unchecked. Just thinking about it exhausts me because I haven't forgotten what that chaos feels like. I am now free of the destructive and limiting cycle of programmed and out of control thinking that I was once a prisoner of. These belief systems *can* be rewritten. I'm proof of this. My mind was chaos and madness for so long, I have a very deep appreciation for the serenity I now experience more often than not.

I want to share that my mind led my life to some very dark and destructive places. I never stopped to think that my mind didn't have my own best interests at heart. Why would I stop to consider that? We tend to grow up pretty self-reliant. No one tells us, *"Hey don't trust that little gremlin voice in there."* But that's the problem isn't it?—I *thought.* All I ever did was think, think, think. And then I thought some more. I couldn't stop thinking. It's my belief that most people who end up on hard drugs do so to *shut their mind up*! And through all that thinking, I forgot to let my heart and spirit speak up to help balance some of that intellectualization. I didn't know at the time this was what I was doing…not consciously anyway. Hindsight is 20/20 right?

Unconsciously, I believe my higher self was screaming at my lower self to wake the fuck up and look at what I was doing. However, because of the blocks in my system, especially around my Ajna and Sahasrara Chakras, the message wasn't getting through. I couldn't hear my higher self calling to me through the roar of my conscious mind and my extremely loud ego. That ego voice has the potential to drown out all messages of sanity when it sees one as a threat to its survival. The ego is a vicious thing when left unchecked in the driver's seat. My Vishuddha (communication center) was way too blocked for me to hear or see the obvious truths no matter how loudly they were screamed.

Here is a visualization I use with my clients: *If you can, imagine me tied up in the back seat of a car while my ego is in the driver's seat careening around with the gas pedal pushed to the floor completely oblivious to my little true self screaming in the back. My true self is tied up, bound, blindfolded, and gagged in the back seat wrestling to break free of the binds. We are speeding along recklessly while I just try to get free.*

Let's take a moment and further discuss this. However, because I am not a doctor of the mind, a psychologist, or anything more than a human sharing my own experience with my own mind, I am going to keep this simple and aligned with my own personal journey about which I am an expert. This is my experience, so it makes me the only expert on it.

For my purposes in this book, we will talk about the conscious, subconscious, unconscious, and ego mind. According to Freud, the conscious mind consists of everything inside of our awareness. This is the aspect of our mental processing that we can think and talk about in a rational way. If we look at something and observe that it's blue, that's the conscious mind making the observation.

However, the information and identification of "blue" comes from the subconscious programming. But in the immediate moment, our interactions, our decisions, our behaviors are made in the conscious mind but based on what the subconscious is whispering. For example, back when I actively decided to make the decision to start smoking cigarettes, that was my conscious mind saying *"Yup, good idea—that will make us cool"* because my subconscious and ego were whispering about how I needed to be cool and bringing up an old stored fear of not being accepted, liked, and good enough.

Subconsciously, I was so programmed to believe I had to fit in somewhere and, at that moment, being a rebel seemed like the perfect fit. I wanted to illustrate this in order to help you see how much happens within the mind that lies underneath one simple decision. But remember this example because we will be returning to it in just a moment. Everything we do is fueled by all of these layers of fears, beliefs, and programming. It was a simplified example that I offered you, but do you see the relationship I am trying to highlight? Good! Now I will ask you to consider and write down what beliefs fuel your behavior.

When we analyze something and decide how we feel about it in the moment, this is our conscious mind again being fed by subconscious programming. In the present moment, where I am free from preconceived patterns and preferences, I can look at a beautiful flower and say, "I like this flower. It is pretty."

In the present, we can just see, observe, and respond accordingly. If I am not in the present, but rather stuck in programming, then my subconscious might come up with something that makes me see the flower and have an aversion to it. Instead of seeing the flower for what it is, I am now seeing it through a filter of past memories and judging it based on that filter of thoughts which, of course, brings on emotions. At this point, everything goes to shit because now I am not here in the moment with the flower and you. I'm, instead, living in the past where I am clouded by who knows what programming that doesn't actually have anything to do with what is occurring in front of us. We just *think* it does.

It seems ingrained and natural that traumatic events and our upbringings would affect us in life, but it's actually not. This is not our true and natural state. Living in the past as a prisoner of our previous experiences and the ensuing filters is a mental cesspool; one that allows us to not take responsibility for ourselves. However, I am pleased to tell you that there is another way. And we will get there.

First though, let's discuss a little more on the mind. Short term memories live in the conscious mind. When we think about the delicious meal we are eating, this is our conscious awareness. When we file away the experiences of the most recent time, they move into the subconscious where they are stored forever and ever to be brought back up and referred to as needed. Think of the subconscious as a massive reference library. Simply put, I like to see it like this: when we are present with appreciation and gratitude in the moment and the now, we are observing the moment with the conscious mind but we are free of any subconscious filters. We just simply are. No filters, no preconceived notions, no opinions. This is the obstacle many people we work with in our Abundant Life Mastery face in discovering the art of being present! It was an obstacle I faced for years.

The trick of being present is to see what's really there in front of us, or inside us, *without its being clouded by the filters of the past.* When we see something we are neutral to it *until our mind creates a thought about what we're observing.* Then emotions arise and the drama unfolds where we create a whole saga based on what becomes a very distorted version of reality. Based on this process, we will find attraction or aversion to whatever we are observing, be it self, others, scenery, or objects. When we can remain present with what is occurring in front of us, we find that we can begin experiencing equanimity, or the practice of being neutral to what is occurring...the practice of seeing things as they are instead of as we think they are.

Now, quickly, come back to those cigarettes with me. For 100 reasons in my subconscious mind that I wasn't aware of at the time, I believed that cigarettes were a good idea for me in that moment. So, now, let's use this to define the subconscious a bit more for our purposes. Let us liken it to the autopilot of the mind. Simply put, the subconscious concerns the part of the mind of which we are not fully aware, but which influences our actions and feelings. So it's like the puppet master, yes? Our programming lives here as do our beliefs, defenses, and emotions.

We also have two powerful energy centers that seek to balance what happens here, the Ajna and Sahasrara. They will align us and work to keep us connected, if we unblock them. The ego is birthed from here and will block our spiritual connection as quickly as it can. The ego is a defense mechanism against emotional shocks and traumas. It has its purpose in identity and individuality, but the ego, left unchecked, is the enemy of consciousness and unity; it must be mastered not the master.

The ego is the place where we create the false and erroneous separation from one another and from Source. If you read Tolle, he talks about how the ego is where we create the "false-sense of self," which is all just an illusion. A healthy ego is a natural and necessary element of the human experience.

When we suffer from energetic blocks and imbalances within the chakra system, the ego kicks into maximum overdrive to cover up our negative self feelings, such as insecurity, low self-esteem, unworthiness, and fear. It wants us to feel safe and secure from the big scary world out there; it wants to be coddled and it doesn't like to be checked. The ego houses our gremlins, our self-limiting narratives, and our inability to truly connect with the true soul essence of who we are (this is a direct threat to the ego!).

Most of us don't consciously walk around acknowledging the ego unless we've done some work to identify and distinguish it from our soul voice, and, thus, we are operating from a point of awareness in a balanced system. From here, we can work to see and observe the thoughts which come from ego and quietly redirect them in order to reprogram our wiring and our beliefs. This begins to take some of the power away from the ego and subconscious. If you're anything like me, your ego has displayed its ability to ghastly misuse its power, so you're now ready to deliver it a well-deserved time out in the corner while your heart and soul take the driver's seat for a while.

Subconscious is also where our preferences live. God knows we've turned into a society that caters to our preferences...a little too much in my opinion. We're breeding a generation that believes we should always just get our way and have what we want. For example, when I look at the object I mentioned observing before saying, *"Oh yes it's blue,"* I know it's blue because my subconscious mind has been programed to recognize the color and attach it to the word blue. If I take a moment here and observe my reaction to blue—do I like it? dislike it? how do I feel about it?–all of this is fed to my conscious mind, where it comes into my awareness from my subconscious mind, which has been programmed through life by my experiences. If I was raised to label this color blue with the word red, then it would be red to me. Not blue. And we could argue for days about that. So you see, I share this to illustrate that thoughts are not necessarily reality. They are quite subjective and quite real to their owners.

All of the things that happened to us in the past–all of the memories that eventually got stored in our long-term memory, all of our lessons, experiences, and traumas–are stored in our subconscious. The manners and ways of behaving our parents may or may not have taught us are programmed into our subconscious. The repetitive math tables and lessons are there. The beliefs we carry about ourselves and the outside world live here. If I got smacked around for crying as a child, eventually my mind came to believe crying was a bad idea as it would result in harsh punishment. I knew if I started to cry, trouble would follow. This belief would be programmed into my subconscious, and I would then lead an entire life believing it was bad to cry.

So until I am ready to address this stored belief in order to heal and balance my system and unlearn these subconscious programmings, I will carry this belief and choose to stuff my emotions. And that's exactly what I did for 34 years until I was finally ready to rewrite some erroneous and detrimental belief systems. That's the one thing I've learned and something that has become the core of my work here; our beliefs can be unlearned and replaced with new ones which better serve our Higher Self and purpose.

I will mention ego frequently as I get back into my personal story. Greater minds than I have studied and written volumes about this part of the human mind. I am not an expert, but I have gained some wisdom from my experiences and have come to believe this: my ego is not my friend. It does not have my higher interests at heart. It is merely akin to a childish, bratty, entitled piece of my mind, one which judges me and beats me up, all while telling me I am separate and different from you, while somehow being simultaneously better than and less than everyone else. Say that five times fast! However that works.

To me, it's the piece of my mind that wants to lock my soul away in a little box deep within me, burying it so no one can ever hurt it because it is so threatened by the world and afraid of pain. That was my story for a very long time and, because of my imbalances, blockages, and my inability to use my inherent Manipura energy to empower myself, my ego almost killed me.

A side note on the ego—human minds are the only minds that develop ego. And when we are blocked and imbalanced in mind, body and soul, the ego becomes the jailer. For me, the ego was where my warped sense of esteem, worth, importance and identity came from. In a sense it's what gives each of us humans our individuality. Animals see themselves as one of a pack or community; they don't have the human ego sense of personal identity like we do. Our ego is what tells us we are unique, separate, and different from one another; that there is no connection between us. And yes, while we all do have our own unique traits, don't be fooled by the ego. *We are all one and we are all connected in a greater consciousness.* Admit it or deny it, the connection is there. If you're in denial, no worries, it's just your ego speaking and you have some work to do. You're in the right place! If you're doubtful but open, this is good...it's progress! Keep going. Shortly we will discuss identities, clinging, attachments, and beliefs, all of which come from the ego mind. When our chakra system is fractured or imbalanced, ego attaches to these behaviors and defines our sense of self based on them. It needs an outside thing to attach to because it fears that it is not real.

The ego feeds the incessant need we have as humans to dominate others with our thoughts and opinions (a sure sign of energetic imbalances and insecurity). It must separate and divide; it labels and judges everyone and everything. It is the voice that says, *"Oh no, we don't like them because they don't act the way we think they should."* It's the voice that says *"You don't agree with me, then you must be stupid."* It is the judge, the jury, and the executioner. It is that voice which clings to those beliefs that someone else put into our minds long ago, and we are subconsciously choosing to keep living our lives according to those beliefs–a task with which the ego happily helps. The belief that says, *"I suck, or if they really knew me they wouldn't love me, I'm a failure, I'll never succeed."* The ego whispers these beliefs at first as it wraps every thread of our existence in these fears. Then it grows into a monster train of thought that becomes so loud. And to make up for those extremely loud beliefs and fears, it starts screaming louder and louder about how much better than everyone else we are, how we don't need anyone anyway.

It's quite paradoxical isn't it? A bit of a mess? I'm not going to lie, it makes me cringe a bit just thinking about it.

However, in a *balanced* system, the ego merely acts as a quiet voice which has some preferences, identities, beliefs, and opinions. It helps us hold boundaries and our personal value. It doesn't run the show anymore, but rather it assists. It may occasionally try to step in, once again trying to wrestle control away and separate us from our collective consciousness and the oneness we have found by living in a balanced system, but when we are balanced and prepared, we see it. We come to be able to observe the ego's tricks and we get to make a choice and say, *"Not today ego, but I appreciate your efforts in trying to separate me from my beautiful harmony with the world."* In balance, it becomes a choice which way we go and how we live. We no longer identify with only the ego-self as our true identity; we see beyond this illusion. We can either be present in the now or we can continue to view everything with a filtered lens from our subconscious and ego, which keeps us playing small and living in the past and the future but never the now. And the now is where the magic happens.

"Your ego is your soul's worst enemy." ~Rusty Eric

Fractured

Chapter 5
Adventures With My Unbalanced Mind

"You can avoid reality but you cannot avoid the consequences of avoiding reality." ~Ayn Rand

Now that we've discussed the human mind and it's properties, let me introduce you, on a more intimate level, to my mind. All of the juicy scandal I promised is being offered to you on a silver platter in order to serve as an excellent, and sometimes ugly, illustration of how the mind can show up to work and cause lots of trouble in a blocked or fractured chakra system.

Are you ready? Buckle your seatbelts!

What a place! I remember the first time I was trying to get off drugs, someone told me, *"Your mind is a dangerous neighborhood. Never go there alone. Especially not early in sobriety."* The problem for me at the time was I liked dangerous neighborhoods. I liked danger, period. There was a very unhealthy lack of conscious fear present in my life back then. I actually preferred the dangerous places to the other parts of society because, at least in a dangerous neighborhood, I knew where the threats were coming from. In my mind, the rest of the world just seemed to be full of hidden threats, minefields, and booby traps where those who were meant to be kind weren't. Where those you were supposed to be able to trust let you down (all due to traumas incurred which then get stored in the Muladhara Chakra and keep us from feeling safe). I felt unguarded, unprepared, and vulnerable in society and around people from the time I was very young. I was overwhelmed by the fact that I could read everyone's emotions and they were some heavy shit. I absorbed everything and it felt like I was drowning all of the time.

To protect myself from this constant feeling of an imminent threat, my ego grabbed hold and took charge early on. Some reasons I will mention here. My mind is quite sharp. It always has been. I learn fast and I see everything. I rarely need to be told something more than once to understand it.

My mind is always working and was from a very young age. Just analyzing away. Now, if I could do anything, I would study the mind, its chemistry, and the intricate workings of it. I would study it to try to find answers to why some minds are so sharp and intuitive–almost clairvoyant and sensitive–while others aren't. I have some hypotheses I would like to test when it comes to the link between the mind and the chakras. Do all minds have the potential to be more sharp, intuitive, and clairvoyant? Yes, I believe so. Is it a soul age connection that has to do with how many times we've jumped in this rodeo called life on Earth? Is it a matter of mental exercise and energetic balance and flow? I believe that it has less to do with the actual physical component of the brain and more to do with the soul energy feeding it, which gives us our knowledge.

Where do you think knowledge comes from? I believe, like any muscle in the body, the brain must be worked out. And it must be energetically balanced too. That being said, I am digressing, so shall we get back to it?

I wasn't aware of this deeper stuff I am throwing out here for most of my life. I wasn't even aware my mind was different than most people's. I didn't know I was an empath and highly intuitive; we didn't use those words in the 80s. Indigo Child? Never heard of one until five years ago. This is exactly where much of my frustration with life, society, and people came from. I didn't understand why people didn't know what I was feeling and thinking when I knew what they were feeling and thinking most of the time. That also explains why I felt so transparent and vulnerable growing up. I felt everyone's stuff so I thought they could see right through me too, and that meant they would know that I felt inadequate, afraid, and stupid.

Furthermore, because of my energetic blocks and imbalances, my mind kicked into overdrive as a defense and I began intellectualizing everything early on as a way to avoid my emotions. As I mentioned when discussing how my blocks affected me physically, this energetic split would get so bad that eventually I wasn't able to get in touch with my emotions at all. I would think about the emotions I should be having and feel nothing.

Come into my world with me for a moment. I've always been very intuitive. My mind has always inherently known things about people and their thoughts, feelings, intentions, wants, needs, desires and so on. As I mentioned, for most of my life, I didn't realize this wasn't the norm for most people. I was frustrated and baffled very early on as to why no one seemed to know what I wanted and needed when I was constantly overwhelmed with knowing what they felt or needed without their telling me. The word empath wasn't floating around back then, and I wasn't aware I was one. All I could think was, *"What about me?"* I was a child and selfish at that point, but I did carry on the theme of self-centered thinking for much of my life, as that's what happens when we are disconnected from our spiritual selves. The mind takes over and, as the ego drives, we forget that we are all one and connected. The world becomes all about us. (Unbalanced Svadhisthana at its best!)

My next thought would be *"Why the hell should I have to explain myself and tell people what I am thinking? They should know! I know about them! Why don't they know?!? Read my mind! I'm reading yours!"* Enter 'shoulds' stage right. Should is a just a world that should go the fuck away, no pun intended. There was a lot of the should word in my vocabulary for a very long time, and I'm guessing if you bring awareness to your own inner narratives you will find it there as well. Should is a word I have gladly discarded, for it no longer serves me. It doesn't serve anything but our ego and expectations.

As a child and teenager, because I was already blocked in my Vishuddha, I had no ability to communicate my frustrations and needs. I was blocked all over. When I reconnect with my early memories, I am overcome with the feelings of frustration at not being able to express myself that cloud every single childhood memory of mine. I have since healed this by returning to the past and revisiting this pain, but it has been a process.

This seems like a good time to share a bit of background so you can see where I come from. Not that it matters, per se, because without every single thing that happened to me I wouldn't be where I am today. I had the experiences I needed for my own personal evolutionary journey. However, I'd like us to relate to one another through our shared experiences. It didn't help matters much that, in my house growing up, we weren't exactly "functional," *whatever that means.*

We were a typical 80s family, or so I thought. My life began in northern New Jersey where I was born to an Italian/English mom and a Cuban dad. And then there were us three kids. I knew from a young age that my sister (the oldest and an only child for a few years) resented the shit out of me, probably for being born. Dad worked hard and Mom stayed home with us. This was possible in the economy of the 1980s. So Mom was around all the time and she catered to us kids. We were her world.

Materialistically, we had what we wanted and needed: cars, toys, clothes, food. All this was more than amply given to us, and we lived comfortably on the material level. We had grandparents around who loved us, too. I was the middle of three, between an older sister and a baby brother. I mentioned in the Body section about my physical inabilities to communicate from early on.

Here, I will talk about how my earliest memories are very emotionally charged. Every memory I revisit has a cloud of emotion attached to it like a sepia filter on Instagram. Some are my emotions and some are other peoples'. All I remember is the emotions surrounding all memories and experiences from very early on. They're just so present.

Little did I know that as I grew up , and as my ego grew, I would cut myself off from those emotions, as they were too overwhelming for my highly-sensitive and unbalanced system to handle. I was not equipped for the emotional nature of life on Earth. (On a side note: During a recent shamanic journey, I connected with a memory of choosing to incarnate on Earth and leaving the higher realms for my experience here. Immediately after that, I connected with one from my first year of life where I was just pissed, confused, frustrated because I felt so limited. What I understood from this memory was that I came to Earth as a spiritual infinite being, was born into a physical body immediately forgetting my higher purpose, and was then like, "what the fuck did I sign up for in this fucked up physical realm called Earth in the limited little body where I couldn't do anything?")

From my earliest recollection, my mind was off and running from the gate. I was always thinking. It was incessant, the amount of chatter going on in my head; I was assessing everything all the time and connecting every event with how they somehow reflected my inherent lack of worth. It was all about me.

My mind was on a constant loop of how stupid and inadequate I was. I would think thoughts, feel ashamed, and then boom—ego would kick in to 'protect' me from those feelings. I was often angry. I believed those feelings I was having as weak and unacceptable; I felt as though if anyone knew how horrible I felt about myself they would know I was indeed horrible.

As empathic as I was, I sensed my sister was resentful at having a new little sister, and my mind never let me hear the end of how I was not wanted. I believe the 'You're stupid' anthem playing in my mind was a carried emotion from my Dad. (Carried emotions are an actual psychological thing, not something I made up). I have yet to ask him if these words were something he heard much growing up, but, through my own process of healing and digging deep, I believe this is where it came from. Because he would often use the phrase, *"What are you stupid?"* anytime we would make mistakes or act badly, I believe it was passed down to him.

I recently found an old black and white photo of my Dad and his own father where he was maybe three of four years old. In this photo, I could see the emotional weight he was already carrying at a young age. It was reflected in his entire stance and body in the photo, and it broke my heart open to know he suffered so much.

The thing that we tend to forget, or never realize until we mature and get our self-centered heads out of our asses, is that we can each only act in ways we know at any given time. Until we know better, we repeat the patterns we are handed when we come into this world. We can't see this when we are smack in the middle of the chaos and disappointment, when we just want parents who show up for us in the ways we think they should, and we instead get hurt and point fingers. At this point, we too don't know any better, just like the people we are blaming for not doing 'better' by us.

I know that it's quite hard to accept this thought in the face of traumas we may be carrying yet unhealed, but it's a very real and true perspective on things. Don't get me wrong. I'm not saying to condone horrific treatment or behavior written off as 'they didn't know any better,' but allowing others the space to err and walk through their own lessons calls for a certain amount of humility on our part. It is also quite freeing.

I understand all of this now, but as a child who just wanted to please my parents and be loved, I internalized those harsh words for a long time. Again, we can't do better than we know how to do at any given moment, and I didn't know how to do any better than that back then. This is all wisdom in hindsight, of course. The point now is that I love my Dad very much, and I no longer blame him for how I'm choosing to live my life. For a long time, I used the emotional abandonment and verbal assaults of my childhood as an excuse to fuel my shitty choices. I kept myself in victim mode so that I wouldn't have to step outside of my comfort zone, which was fortified by anger and energetic brick walls to keep everyone at arm's length. Now that I've freed myself from this false blame and taken responsibility for my life, I am able to see that he did the best he could with what he had been given in life. He loved us in the only ways he knew how, and that's what really counts. To me, that's forgiveness.

We weren't a cult–no one was intentionally programming anyone–but this is very much where the programming begins for us as children. It happens in all families and communities. In childhood we are taught by the actions of the world around us, especially by the people closest to us. Our minds take everything we see, hear, and experience and forms it all into a network of subconscious beliefs. We then build defenses to protect ourselves and keep us in what comes to be known as our comfort zone.

We also subconsciously seek out people, places, and things that will solidify our beliefs as true. In other words, we attract the very events that prove our beliefs to be real and correct. Thus, we shape our own reality. So you see, if these beliefs are not taken out every so often and reevaluated to see if they are still rational and useful, they can become rotten, festering, outdated thorns in our sides. They can hold us back and block us from the true beauty of life.

For example, and I'll just speak from experience here, if we carry a belief that men are no good and will always abandon us, we will energetically attract emotionally unavailable men who can't show up for us the way we think we want them to. Problem is, when we attract one who does, we don't know what to do with that attention. So we continue to seek out the ones who fit the pattern, and then we get to cry about how right we are when they abandon us. It works out quite well for that little ego-self who wants to be alone, surrounded by high walls. Before finding inner balance and a new belief system, I clung so rigidly to my beliefs that I almost died to see them to the end. I didn't want to break!

Now for me, whose mind was super intuitive to everyone else's thoughts, I was picking up on stuff left and right, and my poor little brain was just filing and programming it all away for later use in life. It's amazing what the mind will hold on to, deep within the subconscious, that the ego will later use as the driving forces behind our approach to life.

I wasn't conscious and aware of all of this activity which was brewing beneath the surface of my conscious mind and undermining my every move in life. It just directed and I obeyed. I never questioned. *I didn't know I could*! It said jump, and I said, *"How high?"* I continuously created patterns subconsciously where I would attract the energy I thought I was trying to avoid so my mind could say, *"See look I was right, "* and keep me trapped in victim mode.

When we are victims we don't have to take responsibility for what we are creating. It's much easier. I gave it no thought for many years. It was auto-pilot all the way just like that analogy I gave you earlier where the ego is driving the car like a madman.

Back to the childhood!

There wasn't a whole lot of communication happening in my household growing up. It was pretty much nonexistent. We just didn't talk about stuff. There was no encouragement, tons of criticism, and not much outward nurturing. My parents did what they knew and they showed up for us in the ways that they knew how; one of which was *not* communication. Dad instead provided for us financially and that was that; it's how he shows love still to this day. He's a man of few words.

Again, hindsight is 20/20, and I know this now, but back then I just equated his lack of affection and nurturing into rejection circling around my not being good enough. Thus one of the first belief systems I grabbed hold of was the belief I was not good enough to be loved in the way that I was looking for. It hurt to feel rejected and not good enough, but I couldn't express this. I can see it now...myself as a child asking to talk to my parents and coming out with how I'm a highly intuitive empath, and I need them to be more sensitive to my emotional needs. It's too funny to imagine! It was the 80s and people just didn't talk about stuff like this. My parents come from a different generation. Not wrong, not right. Just *different.*

I would carry this mindset of not being good enough throughout most of my life. Keep in mind that these belief systems we install and carry can weigh on us energetically as well. Diverting off the path of your soul purpose because of a belief that you need to get a real job can put some pretty serious blocks in place at the Solar Plexus and Throat Chakra levels. For me, my mind started to tell me that if I could just be better and more perfect and not break stuff, or make stupid mistakes, maybe he would love me the way I was seeking.

It all comes down to the love languages we understand, but, as children, we don't have the world awareness to see that someone is doing what they know and that it has nothing to do with us. It's not until we grow up and clear away the filters that we can see the truth. Thus I wallowed in shame, insecurity, anger, and confusion as to my role and place in the world. I didn't understand the working of my mind and emotions, so my ego went rampant and formed a defense around me; one which had me believing it was safer not to let anyone know I cared. It told me not to let anyone in and just be a hard ass.

It's so funny to me now as I write it because it's such a ridiculous thought pattern to live by, but this mentality ruled me and is exactly what almost killed me in my adult years. The insane belief that said, "*If I could just be perfect...*"

Ah yes, perfectionism. We all know it, and many of us suffer from it. If you don't personally suffer from perfectionism, I'm sure you know someone who does.

Perfectionism is an ISM all to itself which brings me to the darkest part of my tale and the first section in recognizing blockages and imbalances of the mind— the presence of the ISMs.

"The great blessings of mankind are within us and within our reach; but we shut our eyes, and like people in the dark, we fall foul upon the very thing we search for, without finding it." ~Seneca

****If this book is resonating with you, and you are not yet part of our facebook community, join us now! www.facebook.com/groups/hugyourchaos and www.facebook.com/groups/chakrachaos

Chapter 6
Symptoms of An Unbalanced Mind - The Isms

"There is no chemical solution to a spiritual problem."
~Unknown

Because the isms wrought such havoc and destruction in my life, I will start with them. What is an ism? you may be asking. Well I'm sure you've probably experienced at least one if you're reading this, or at least know someone who has. I myself suffered from alcoholism, perfectionism, workaholism, escapism while also being the victim of many other isms - sexism, misogynism, feminism. All the isms so present in the world. You name it.

Let's talk about what an ism is now. Ism—I , self, me. People who suffer from isms are self-obsessed. And yes, I was obsessed with myself. I was living in the childish place of ego where my only concern was my needs and desires and no one else's. The world revolved around me and my security. This was my driving subconscious belief system for a long time. Of course, now I understand that it was purely a defense mechanism because I had no ability to handle life as a sensitive person, but it sure caused a lot of destructive chaos in my life. The severe energetic blockages in my chakra system were manifesting as addictions by the time I was 15, and emotional disorders much earlier than that. I didn't know how to interact with the world in a healthy manner so it was easier to obsess on myself and my needs. I literally felt as though I couldn't process anything on an emotional level, so it became easier to just shut down.

What I didn't know back then was emotions are just energy, and mine could not flow. I didn't know it was energetic blockages I was suffering from. In order to let go of any emotions, but especially pain, the energy needs to flow through and be released. Mine was just getting stuck. I looked like an adult and acted like a child internally, and sometimes outwardly, if I may admit, and I would be trapped living in that space into my 30s.

My mental/emotional body fractured from both my physical and spiritual bodies. There was a split. A separation. No connection. Thus, I operated from a place of selfishness, conceit, self-centeredness, and ego. To my understanding, I believe that when we are living in a state of disconnection and brokenness where we operate from our intellect and ego in order to avoid our emotions, it often manifests as addiction. Keep in mind that addictions can be to *anything*–not just alcohol, drugs, sex, etc. The root of addiction is simply disconnection. We seek connection and look to outside people, substances, or activities to help us feel connected. For a time it works. Eventually, we discover we are still disconnected and merely masking this feeling. It's like putting a Band-Aid on a gunshot wound.

To further explore my point for a moment, when I say addiction I refer to many things. Society wants to put alcoholism and drug addiction into this little box, as though they're different than one's addiction to sugar or food, shopping or gambling. At present, humans are addicted to thinking, chaos of the mind, avoidance, fear, and blame. These are all tricks of the mind so it can try to maintain an illusion of control, self, disconnection. The ego wants to stay in charge. To illustrate, in the same way many people can't understand why I couldn't just stop shooting cocaine and heroin even though I was destroying my life, I once couldn't understand why an obese person, who suffers from high blood pressure and already had one heart attack, can't stop eating double bacon cheeseburgers chased down with soda. Now, as a result of my own journey and ever growing understanding of the energetic nature of life, I understand this is but a symptom of a greater, deeper problem–disconnection and energetic blockages.

Now back to me! My favorite topic…

My ego sought to separate me from the world. It sought to divide and explain everything and to make it all more complicated than it is. (That's what the go does! The ego's fuel is the illusion of separation.) Mine succeeded for the many years that I was trapped in darkness, isolation, and addiction. I wanted to avoid anything I considered 'painful' or unpleasant. I avoided talking about emotions and I was incapable of getting real and vulnerable. I was scared to death of dwelling in the realm of the emotional body, and I had no idea. Now I understand that this was my path individually, as it is for so many others, and is also currently the collective plague of humanity. I recognize it so well because I lived it.

It's as simple as this — the need to reach outside of ourselves to feel okay is simply a manifestation of a fractured, imbalanced, or out of whack chakra system. In my opinion, it's even further linked and solidified by the programming incurred through our current society and media outlets. Everything tells us that the answer to our problems can be found in a pill, outfit, person, place, thing, event, activity, or task *outside of ourselves.* We don't hear advertisers telling us to see the connection within because that *would dampen their sales and profits*! That's a topic for a whole different book though, so I'll save it for then.

It seems to me that the severity of the symptoms being displayed is merely a reflection of how bad the fracture is. Is it just a block or have we indeed fractured and broken away from the various bodies? It appears as though humanity as a whole is suffering from this in so many ways. In current times, as a result of energetic blockages and imbalances, we over think, under-feel, avoid, blame, and simply stay stuck as prisoners of our own minds.

As for my blockages, like I mentioned, I had a severe fracture and blockage at the level of my Vishuddha and Anahata Chakras. I had under- and over-active energies in most of my system, but these two were full on blocked.

I was completely blocked at that point of my life. There was no flow of energy through my system. My split was so severe, it manifested in one of the worst addictions possible—intravenous use of heroin and cocaine, the hardest drugs out there. I couldn't process emotions so I just denied them, attempting to bury them until I could no longer feel anything. My mind incessantly kicked the shit out of me no matter what I achieved or accomplished. I had no idea who I was or who I wanted to be. I gave up on being anything more than what I was -- a junkie. I was a victim of life. I had no clue that I already had a deep well of personal power lying untapped in my Manipura Chakra. I wanted to be saved, but I couldn't ask for help. And I certainly didn't know or understand that I had the power within me to help myself. What a concept, right?

Somewhere within me, I knew that I certainly wasn't born to live a life on the streets as a strung out criminal. That was by no means my highest potential, but, at the time, I believed it was. However, I now see that the experience was necessary for me to gain the wisdom and learning I have. I also believe that we choose the lessons that we come to Earth to learn for the evolution of our own soul essences. Without my experiences, I would not be here or able to pass it on to all of you, my fellow seekers and sufferers.

I was born a kind soul, albeit a frustrated one. I didn't understand the world around me at all as a child. My earliest memories of my thoughts perceived the world as overwhelming and threatening. I wanted to force my will at a very young age, and was very trapped in feelings of frustration over my inability to adequately express my thoughts, feelings, or intentions. I could read the world around me, and I knew what others were thinking and feeling very early on. The fact that no one could seem to read my emotions and thoughts frustrated the shit out of me. No one was talking about indigo children and empaths in the 80s.

Naturally, my mind was a battle ground from very early on; it was a bully. Thus when I found the things (books, alcohol, drugs) that would shut it up I grabbed hold of those things and wouldn't give them up for the life of me. Now it makes sense that my mind was such a noisy chaotic place because the energetic flow was sluggish throughout my body. My excessive Ajna energy was just getting stuck there—like a pinball launched in a machine, my thoughts just careened through my mind with nowhere to go, incessantly telling me how useless and terrible I was. Also known as the monkey mind, as we like to call it in Buddhism.

Let's go back for a moment.

I met alcohol quite young. Booze was always around my life in the 80s. My Dad drank beer–always beer–and when he drank, he was fun. He laughed, joked, played music, and acknowledged us. He seemed happy. When it was the weekend and the party was on, things were fun. When the party wasn't on and the beer wasn't flowing, Dad was not so nice. He was angry, and my mind told me that it was all my fault. I thought he hated me. I thought it was a direct reflection of my worth. I thought the world revolved around me. I wasn't able to see the bigger picture, and I wouldn't see it for 33 years. Alcohol, for me, was attached to ideas of glamour, fun, and being an adult. So naturally when I got to try it for the first time, I loved it. I felt mature, capable, and good enough.

Our parents used to let my sister and me share a wine cooler here and there when we would be out on the lake, and we thought we were just the coolest. Again, 80s parenting was vastly different to the organic, hand sanitizer, clean, electronic parenting we see nowadays, so it really wasn't a big deal. I mean we ate dirt and glue and somehow managed to survive. My sister was older than me by two and a half years, and I idolized her. She seemed to have it all together. And she had no problem bossing me around.

Another trick of my mind with the bully in my head was the constant comparison of myself to everyone else to hammer the belief home of how much I sucked. (Much of this comes from our Manipura, or Solar Plexus, Chakra which governs our self-worth and identity. I believe the imbalance of this particular chakra heavily plays a part in the 'ISMs' that show up throughout our lives. This is due to the fact that when our chakras are healthy, balanced, and flowing properly we have no need for 'ISMs' because we are whole, complete, and comfortable in our identities and ourselves. The need for the escapes provided by 'ISMs' fades away.)

Back to myself as an emotionally heavy, energetically overburdened little girl sharing a wine cooler with my sister. Our extended family used to look at me and sing my praises and tell me how smart I was. Yet, I just didn't see it. My grandma used to tell me I was special. Never in a million years would anyone have thought that I was going to be fated to walk the hallowed and dangerous streets of Newark, New Jersey with a needle in one arm and a crack pipe in my pocket. But, yes, that innocent little girl was to become a psychotic, strung out junkie who was driven–like a vampire for blood–after the warm, euphoric numbness and quieting of the mind that heroin would bring. Heroin exists for a reason and it sure does the job well of numbing the pain. Not only is it physically addictive, but it works so well against pain that you can't help but want to keep doing it.

I didn't go right for the hard stuff; it was a gradual progression of the mind that led to me the dirtiest of dirties - heroin. To be fair, it wasn't all that gradual considering I was strung out at age 18, but I've never been one to do things really slowly. We boozed it up here and there through our junior and high school years. When we could, we would steal booze from our parents liquor bottles and fill them back up with water. I personally would smuggle vodka and fruit punch–who remembers that nasty Minute Maid super sweet fruit punch?–into school to be a rebel. Or we would steal a crisp, cold can of Busch beer from the fridge, which tasted like piss but was forced down for the effect anyways. Later I would grow to love the taste of beer, but at that age I just wanted to look cool and get drunk.

I remember the first time I got really drunk. We were on Long Beach Island at the Jersey Shore, and we had a bottle of SoCo–Southern Comfort—the classy girl's drink of the 90s. Oh God was it gnarly going down. It was horrid. The burning and the taste, and then the warmth of the effect. But I chugged it down anyways because I wanted to look tough and cool. For some reason, at the age of 14 or 15, I had it in my head that being able to chug down mass amounts of hard liquor was something to be proud of. In my mind, that ability gave me swagger and street cred, even then. It made me tough and filled this sense and need I had to be a badass. I know...priorities, right?

Needless to say, the warm, brown substance worked magic for me. All of a sudden, I was pretty enough, smart enough. I was no longer self-conscious. my head stopped telling me how much I sucked and how inadequate I was. *My head was quiet and I could finally just be.* I finally felt like I fit somewhere and my mind gave it a rest beating me up for the first time in my life. The anxiety faded away with each swig of SoCo I took. Thus my first outside substance related 'ISM' was born. Hello booze, goodbye anxiety. Chakra imbalance fed frustration, what? Not that I was consciously aware that this was my problem back then, but it didn't matter, booze made it all go away. Sweet oblivion was mine.

Naturally, I graduated quite quickly to bringing vodka and fruit punch with me to school during my freshman year of high school. I kept it in a Lion King Thermos no less. Why not hide my booze in a Disney themed plastic kiddie cup, because what could be more of a paradox? Me as an underage teen, socially awkward and scared to death, so lost beyond the wall of ego I had built to hide my inadequacies that I was convinced I had to present a tough bitch to the world. So why not smuggle booze in a Disney cartoon kids cup? I wasn't giving it that much though at the time, but it just felt right for my image back then.

At this point in my life, everything I did was to make me look cool, be cool, and appear as if I didn't give a fuck about anything. I was angry inside but I didn't know it, and I was launching a full scale mission of self-destruction to show the world just how much I thought it sucked. I believe this is where my full energetic and emotional fracture really happened, because, from here on out, I really couldn't get in touch with any semblance of my feelings, especially not those of caring about anything. I couldn't get in touch with *any* feelings really. I was dwelling and living from my intellectual mind, which was a nasty little bully, so I actively tried to shut it up with anything I could find to get away from it. It was around this time that I quit doing all the things I enjoyed–the team sports like cheerleading and softball–and I sold myself out. Those things had been helping me grow as a person, to develop some self-worth here and there, and I walked away from them in order to feel accepted and look cool in the eyes of my peers. Thus, the fracture was complete, and I would spend years living in addiction and 'ISMs' trying to silence my nasty little ego mind.

Drugs naturally made their appearance in my life and, in the true nature of a sell out, I tried every single one presented to me whether I liked it or not. The word 'No' didn't exist for me. I would continue to do any one of the substances at hand even if I didn't like the effects produced by it, had never heard of it, or had any qualms about taking it. My mind told me I had to or everyone would judge me and my mind was boss. And I just wanted my ego mind *to shut the fuck up*. My mind was the king. It said jump and I said how high. As smart as I was, I didn't know any better. I couldn't see it.

High school was a mess. I vacillated between wanting to do good and turn myself around, and not quite being able to break free from the identity and image I was claiming at the time. I would show so much potential some days when I would ace tests, get A's and participate, only to turn around and break out in a fit of rebellion–smuggling booze, smoking on the grounds, sitting in Chemistry class stoned on test day as I tried to make sense of the elements–to getting thrown out of class for refusing to hand my pager over to my Algebra teacher. (Yes, I said pager. Anyone who was anyone had a pager in those days). My ego told me I was somebody, and I had to live up to that. My energetic blocks were manifesting in behavioral problems but nobody looked at it like that. "*It's just a phase*," they would say.

My mind wanted me to believe I was invincible, all-important, all-knowing, and that I didn't give a shit. And I listened to it. I've now come to believe that when we have a severe fracture or blockage somewhere in our chakra system, another area is going to kick into overdrive to try to carry the weight of our existence. In my case, it was my mind and my ego that was taking over, and I was, unknowingly, bearing witness as I drove my life to the brink of non-existence while merrily laughing in the passenger seat. I thought it was all just a joke; I truly had a sick sense of invincibility. I just *never* stopped to think about consequences. *Ever.* By the time I found the heroin and the needle, I was so jaded and bitter that I was still laughing in the face of all of it. My ability to give a fuck was buried. With all my brilliance and talent, I was 18 years old, I had barely graduated high school, I said whatever to college, and I was just 'living for the moment'. Or so I told myself. Nothing could get me to care by this point. I just didn't. I had no idea where I was going, no idea what life was about, and no comprehension of what I was missing out on. The flight from reality was in full effect, and I was in some serious denial long before I was actually physically strung out on the drugs.

The denial looked a little like this: if anything came up which didn't suit me and my idea of living, I denied it. Once a problem got too big for me, or too much for me to handle, if I couldn't think my way out of it, I would just run. Boom. Disappear. When I was facing prison time for felony burglary and theft at the age of 20, it still didn't hit home for me that there were real consequences to my actions. I just did what I needed to do to stay high and stay numb. I had no reaction to the fact that *I might get locked up for 3-5 years to state prison.* All I cared about and all that mattered was would I be able to get high in there.

When the detectives came for me, they took me in and locked me up for the charges, and I didn't crack. I lay there in my cell, dope sick, sweating, and cringing. Not once did I say to myself *"Oh shit, I'm in trouble."* No, I just lay there and thought, *"Can we get this over with so I can go get high please?"* So, in a very distorted sense of the idea, as a junkie, I really did live in the moment and for the moment. All I ever concerned myself with was getting the dope into my body at any given moment. There was no anxiety about the future and no remorse about the past. The only catch is that it's not *really* living; it's more like just existing in the moment as a non-entity. More like a zombie than anything else–a non-conscious, energetically fractured blob of a being in a half-dead body running along on autopilot, and floating along from fix to fix, drug to drug. And all the while, my mind was telling me it was okay, and that I *wanted* this life. There was no problem with any of it. My heart was so buried and I was so split from my emotions, I thought I was in agreement. I thought I wanted it. I thought it was easier.

I remember most recently, at the very end for me just before I died, I was sitting there in the darkness of the rickety little crack house studio apartment in Mammoth Lakes, California. I wanted to die. I couldn't carry on with the effort it took any longer to stay high, and the drugs had long since stopped numbing the pain. I was chasing an elusive ghost of a memory from long ago and I was badly falling behind the chase. I was telling myself, *"Well someone has to live this life, right? It's all that's meant for me. I'm meant to live this miserable, hopeless life as a strung out junkie."*

There was mail piled up on the table from all of the debts, court notices, warrants, and who knows what else. I hadn't slept in days because, by this point, I was shooting up 4 grams of cocaine a day and I was almost insane. I couldn't stay out of the bathroom to fix myself for longer than 20 minutes at a time. I was swallowing anywhere from 25-40 opiate painkillers, depending what I could get my hands on. If I got shootable painkillers, I slammed them instantly. I was rife with abscesses from using old dirty needles and cotton as I would struggle to find usable veins in my body. I would swallow a handful of pills, and my body would reject them and I would throw them up into the sink so I didn't lose them. You better believe I would pick the pills up and re-swallow them. It had become a mechanical compulsion to just keep putting shit into my body in the hopes that something–*anything*–was going to do the trick and numb the pain. Or kill me. Whichever happened first.

All I managed to do, all day long, was pump my body full of whichever various substances I could find to shoot, smoke, drink, snort, or swallow. There I was—I who had thought so highly of myself, and thought myself so capable–sitting there, shattered. Broken. I was defeated, and I wanted to die. I, who had gotten accepted into a competitive RN school with a 4.0 GPA, travelled around the world exploring foreign wonders and cities, loved and almost married, outwardly 'had it all' at one point in my blurred history.

There I was, sitting there having convinced myself that all I was capable of and meant to be doing was being a strung out, underfed, cracked out, hopeless, lonely, sad, bitter, jaded, and hateful shell of a human. The delusion was so strong, I saw no problems with any of this in my mind.

My mind had me trapped in a cage, and I was dying. I couldn't even hear myself raising a cry of defense any longer. That little voice of my heart center had been completely buried for a long time now. I was 34 years old and I had nothing to live for anymore.

Shortly after that day, I killed myself.

"Death - the last sleep? No, it is the final awakening."
~Walter Scott

***If you or someone you know is struggling with addiction or alcoholism I highly suggest 12-step programs and recovery homes. Please see my reference section in the back of the book for resources! It's almost impossible to do it alone!

Chapter 7
The Manifestation of Judgement

"Love is the absence of judgement" ~Dalai Lama

It's so funny to me now when I look back on it all and I see how I really, for a long time, thought I was this nonjudgmental and loving person. The reality couldn't have been any further from what I was telling myself I was. In truth, I loathed myself, so how could I truly love others?

I was so caught up in my own selfish needs, expectations, and demands that I was incapable of self-sacrifice for anyone outside of ME, which is the furthest behavior from love there is. And my mind was my harshest judge. It never stopped with its incessant judgmental inner tirades, so, naturally, I was projecting that outward in quiet scorn and judgments on everyone else. I had an inner opinion of everyone and everything and I used my disdain to cement the walls between them and me. You name it and I had an opinion or an expectation that wasn't being met. No one treated me the way I thought I should be treated, and I resented every single one of them for it. But we'll get more into resentment shortly, when we talk about emotions. For now, I want to discuss how the ego-mind will use opinions, judgement, attachments, and beliefs to form our identities into rock solid cement, and then we cling to those identities because the ego-mind tells us we need the identity to feel secure. It perceives a threat in connection and oneness.

This is all a lie. I never knew it though until I finally came to realize how erroneous my thinking was. Thanks to the wisdom of my lived experiences, I now believe the power my mind once had over me was fueled by the energetic fractures and blockages in my chakra system. So naturally, just like I clung to my addictions and had to die before I would surrender them, I also clung to my identities.

Remember when I mentioned how I always had to maintain my 'image' in the eyes of others? It's all related and interconnected. I was one of those nightmare people that–God forbid–someone challenged me on a belief or thought, or didn't fit in with my idea of how my world *should* be, then they were getting critically judged and condemned in my mind, and that's where I would cut them off because I had no use for them. My ego-mind used whatever I didn't like–which was pretty much everything they did–about anyone to keep on cementing and building those walls up around my soul. It was my way of keeping myself separate in order to give my ego exactly what it wanted, because the ego thrives on disconnection. Disconnection from the soul, from Source, God, each other, and all that is. Naturally, then, the ego fuels our 'ISMs' as they all have a common goal–separation from our true essence.

I didn't know yet that everything I was judging in others was just a reflection of what I didn't like about myself, or that I was criticizing something they had or did because I was just jealous that I couldn't or didn't have that thing. Madness right? I hadn't come to see that we are all just mirrors of one another reflecting back the energy we are putting out into the world. I didn't know that the world was an energetic place and that like energy attracts like energy. Thus, whatever is showing up for us carries a lesson. I just blamed because that's all I knew how to do, and my ego-mind loved it.

Let's use relationships as an example. I used to mock any couples who I saw acting all lovey-dovey with one another. Ugh. Love? GTFO! I criticized them as lame, and told myself I didn't want that shit anyway. Ugh, no thank you. I believed that it was true for a long time too. For years, I would just use the guys I met, hook up with them, and discard them to feed my ego. Or, when they did act like decent guys, I labelled them as stage 5 clingers and ran far far away. My inner narrative would be like, *"What do you mean you want to talk to me? Who does that? Go away Needy McNeederson."* You see, I was attracting dudes that would fulfill my inner belief system when it came to the world–the one that said *"You can't count on anyone. You're weird and people don't get you."* I would then act accordingly and blame them, so I could say *"See what I can do? I'll show you. I'll hurt you before you hurt me."* Later, when I got deep into my own shadows and chaos and dug out my belief systems, I, of course, found out that I was too scared to let anyone in and too scared to be vulnerable because my mind was telling me everyone was going to hurt me anyway. Rather than take a chance, I would criticize, blame, judge, insult, and condemn to keep my heart hardened against other people. I was too afraid no one would like the real me. I was so scared to death of pain and rejection that I would risk my life to avoid it.

Even my "close" friends were kept at arm's length. I did this by focusing on their flaws instead of their strengths. I had a few friends I genuinely cared for, but I kept them out there at arm's length, holding everything inside, until I said they could come closer. *But not too close.* And, even then, I didn't really let them in. I just showed up for them. *Okay now that's enough. Go back out. You're threatening me. You're too close.* That's the dance I did for years. One face I gave to the world was this ride or die bitch, down for anything, crazy adrenaline hunting joker. Another that was kept locked inside under protective custody at all costs was hard, wounded, hateful and bitter to cover up the scared little girl I was carrying so deeply within me that I didn't even know she was there.

When I found out I had cancer, I was scared, but I couldn't actually connect with it at the time. Instead of reaching out to my friends, I retreated further within myself. I listened to that judgmental ass, bitchy inner narrative vice who pointed out all the ways everyone was failing me in my time of need, and I grew more and more bitter, judgmental and opinionated. I clung even more deeply to my established identities of that time–which were workaholic, jokester, sarcastic bitch, and fanatical sports fan. I created and set the stage, and *then I judged everyone for playing the roles I assigned them.* Isn't it chaos?

I would allow nothing to get in the way of my work, not even my chemotherapy, because, of course, money had replaced my drug addiction at this stage of life. I was 25 years old and, for a few years, instead of being strung out, I was a workaholic and a travel junkie. (I know some of you may be saying 'at least it's not heroin,' but to me it's still not balance and alignment.) Inwardly, my narrative whispered how '*I worked harder and better than everyone else, therefore this made me better than them. I didn't need them anyway.*' It was just constant judgments as my ego-mind danced between 'not good enough' and 'better than you.' I was an egomaniac with an inferiority complex. Explain that one!

There was no part of me that would show any of you this. I had to carry it all alone. By my mid-20s, I had developed such a persona of 'fuck the world, I'll just make a joke about everything' that no one knew how horrid my mind was on the inside. I joked around a lot and kept my angry scorn and bitterness simmering within. No one knew how mean I was to myself and to everyone around me. The judgments stayed in my mind. And I hid it well. I had a strong persona for the world that most people couldn't see through.

That's the thing about being an empath–you can develop very strong defenses, if you put your mind to it. It's not a pleasant way to live. It's quite ugly and very lonely.

My mind was programmed to believe I could fix myself from outside, and all of the ways I was living and choices I was making were just attempts to do exactly this. The problem was I didn't know exactly what I was trying to fix. My beliefs told me that my opinions defined me, and that if you didn't agree with me, I was better than you. I believed that the world owed me something; I was massively entitled. My mind said I should be praised and rewarded for doing my job as well as for even having a job. At 24, I reentered the world sober for the first time since I was in my teens, and I thought the world owed me something. I still carried a completely bad attitude, blame, resentment, and utter disregard for the true purposes and meanings of life. I had an opinion on politics and an opinion on religions. I hated everything and these polarized issues made it quite easy for me to hate most people as they helped solidify my belief that the world was full of weak minded or ignorant people who were below me.

When it came to religions, if anyone mentioned a God, they were immediately classed into the lame box in my mind and left there. Politics...if you didn't agree with me, you were close-minded. Ha! Who was the close-minded one?!? Me. I know, it's no wonder I got high, right? Could you live with that never-ending storm of judgments and commentaries about everyone? It's exhausting. I probably would've opted for a lobotomy had it been offered. The constant internal narrative of bitterness is no easy pill to live with! Drugs shut that up.

I look back on the beliefs I held, and they are so limited and funny to me now. Thank God we get to rewrite our belief systems at any time we see fit, otherwise I would still be a close-minded, disempowered, bitter, drug addicted brat waiting for the world to reward her. This was honestly my subliminal thought process and mindset for years. It was a living nightmare.

Looking back at myself, I can't help but smile at my folly. I am thankful I freed myself from the bonds of clinging, attachment, and ego identity. And you can, too.

"To see ourselves in everyone we meet, to realize that we are but a reflection of everyone we see, and they of us - this is truly divine." ~Unknown

Chapter 8
Let's Talk About Fear

"The only thing we have to fear is fear itself."
~Franklin Delano Roosevelt

Fear. Once a word that made me cringe with denial, fear is now one of my favorite subjects. Fear fascinates me. I was a completely fear based person for years, not that I was aware of or would have admitted it even if I had realized it. (If I knew then what I know now...) Until about the age of 30, I was convinced I was fearless thanks to the whispers of my ego. I thought because I did hard drugs, committed crimes, robbed drug dealers, went to jail, roamed the streets and projects of Newark, NJ alone, jumped out of planes skydiving, snowboarded big mountains, and basically just acted like an all-around jerk, that I was fearless. Because I was the first one to stand up and say, "let's do it" to someone's crazy idea, I thought I was tough and a badass, which to my deluded mind translated into fearlessness. I thought that, because I was often the ringleader in really bad ideas, I was brave.

Come to find out, I wasn't brave at all. Come to find out, the more extreme my behaviors were, the bigger the fears were that I was attempting to hide with my outlandish, risky, and extreme choices. I still have to laugh as I write about it because the fact that I can put this on paper in a book for the masses to read shows just how far I have come and how much I have changed from the fractured, blocked, fearful, and unbalanced being I was.

Really quickly let's just visit the definition of fear.

> ***Fear*** *- (N) a distressing emotion aroused by impending danger, evil, pain, etc., whether the threat is real or imagined; the feeling or condition of being afraid.*

Most of the time, fear is a trick of the mind. It is an emotion created by the ego when it perceives some threat to itself. We tell ourselves that there is a threat and that we may be in peril from this perceived threat, thus we feel scared. Fear serves its purpose when the threat is actually real, as in some shady person creeping on us in a dark alley, or things that go bump in the night.

Fear bids us to act cautiously, and rightfully so. The problem is when the perceived threat is not real, but, rather, a figment we see as real through the filters of our unhealed traumas and emotional baggage. For example, fear of rejection, not being good enough, failure, vulnerability, etc. Fear is what the mind creates to stop us dead in our tracks from exploring what it sees as a threat any further. It is what stops us from observing and examining the perceived threat to find out if it is actually something that can harm us. Fear says things like, 'turn away; don't look here; you don't want this; don't even try; you're going to fail; don't bother' all the way down to, 'oh my God this is going to KILL you, HURT you, MAIM you. RUN!'

As I have come to balance, I have learned that when I feel fear, I can use this to bring my attention to what it is I am fearing. I can analyze it, observe it, dig into it, and rationally come to a conclusion of whether or not there is a real threat. Then I can make a decision. Is the threat imminent? Is it even real? Do I need to respond? Can I just actually observe a little longer, and trust that what I am fearing is here to help me grow and push me outside my comfort zone? Can I pause and see how my mind creates irrational fear around events which, when I stop viewing them with filters from my past have no real threat? They aren't actually as bad as I make them out to be. Can I get to the root cause of this fear? Almost every time you dig deep enough you will find there is some perceived threat to your survival buried beneath what seems to be a benign thought steering you away from trying something new.

Keep in mind, anything and everything has the possibly to hurt us. Let me show you. An innocent pebble on the street could lodge itself into my foot and it would hurt. But do I then walk around in fear of stepping on a pebble every time I take a step outside, convinced every pebble out there is out to get me? No. A car could kill me any day I leave the house, yet I don't live in fear of this happening 24 hours a day. I probably have more of a chance of getting run over by said car, than I do of being poisoned by a spider, yet I struggle immensely in the presence of spiders...much more so than cars.

Why, then, do we convince ourselves that we need to fear intimacy and vulnerability with people? This is due to the filters that we see the world through; filters that were put in place during our early formative years on the planet. We fear intimacy because we fear pain, and we fear pain because we are programmed to believe we should live a life of no emotional pain, which is, of course, completely erroneous societal programming.

We have watched for years as others have crumbled under the weight of emotional pain because they too were unbalanced, blocked, or fractured, and had no ability to work through it in order to come out more compete on the other side, thanks in part to the modern world's inability to talk about unpleasant experiences and emotions in an open and loving manner. Instead, we learn from people who were taught to avoid anything unpleasant at all costs. We learned from others who were unbalanced. We were raised by people who were suffering. Thus, they inadvertently passed their blocks and suffering onto us. The amount of transgenerational trauma and patterns that gets passed down is insane.

We also suffered things in our life that perhaps traumatized us early on, and because we were not yet independent enough to have come into our own ability of balancing our systems, we carried those traumas and scars, allowing them to fracture, block, and unbalance us. We allowed them to close us off because we didn't know another way. Thus, the cycle just keeps repeating itself until WE decide to stop it within our own life. Then we can't pass it on to others. It isn't anyone's fault, really, because we don't know what we don't know, until we know. However, in this day of information and technology, there are no more excuses for not doing better. We have to be the change we want to see, and this starts with this very topic. Which brings me back to fear. We must step outside of the comfort zone.

What I have come to learn, starting with my own life, is that we sit in our little comfort zones, whatever they may be, not realizing we are missing out on so much living and so much potential. We don't even see that we are missing out on exactly what it is that life is all about. We don't know we are doing it. We don't do this consciously, but we do it. We are taught not to challenge ourselves, to just put our heads down and follow the rules. To conform. Don't make trouble; don't speak up. This is an individual issue as well as societal. We get the double dose of fear programming everywhere we turn. We are taught and we learn fear everywhere, from very early on, and this is growing to an all-time high as I write this. We are being taught to fear everyone and everything these days. As children, we misbehave, and we suffer the consequences. Perhaps our parents suffered greatly from emotional and communication chakra blockages (as mine did), and they do not have the ability to express themselves in a healthy and constructive manner. Maybe they lash out in anger, physically or verbally (mine did). This hurts us. Keep in mind that words hurt more than slaps. Words leave a deep mark. We feel hurt and rejected, or we feel stupid and foolish for making a mistake. We translate it into it being our fault. There is something wrong with us for bringing on the punishment (my beliefs for most of my life). Fear is born.

We go through life in fear of making mistakes because, from very early on, we were taught mistakes and misbehaving brings punishment, and punishment means there is something wrong with us which makes us less lovable. And so, when we go back to our earliest selves before all the dramas, we find our true nature is indeed one of infinite love. We come into the world expecting love because we are so freshly removed from God, the Source, which is infinite divine love. We are then born into this earthly life to a cold, stark world that we can't make sense of with the limited human intellect of a baby. Underneath all other traits we display, we *all* really just seek to give love and receive love. In the blockage of this energy early on, much damage is accrued. This is exactly where we see the massive energetic imbalances that feed the destructive and atrocious behaviors we see at play so rampantly in the world right now. Most behavioral issues can be rooted back to a denial, blockage, or trauma related to love or lack thereof at an early, formative stage in life. Some of this is psychology and some is just obvious once you get deep into energy work.

Let's spend a little more time discussing early fear programming. Early on, we learn mistakes are bad, as was the case in my life. Speaking up against something we don't agree with gets us punished, so we learn to shut up. Why then, as adults, would we ever stop on our own accord and say, *"Let me try something new and different, let me push out of what is comfortable."* We wouldn't. We first have to unlearn the false ego-mind belief that our lives are supposed to be full of stability and comfort before we become willing to push ourselves into the unknown.

We have this need for security so we create this illusion of what we think and feel like gives us this needed security. This is all to fill a hole left by a lack of faith in something bigger. We find true security in the uncertainty of life within the heart center and the soul. Where we get mixed up is that we seek it with the intellect, which tells us the security is found out there...outside of us. So fear tells us to stay put. Fear comes from ego-mind, but, remember, the ego-mind only wants one thing: to protect us, keep us safe, and separate us because separate is what it perceives as safe. It will convince us we must stay right where we are in our illusion of security.

This brings me back to the pebble. As I mentioned, I don't walk around fearing every pebble is out to get me. However, there are people currently living who are so swamped in fear, they are threatened by everything. Like me once, not that I would've admitted it at the time. I was threatened by emotional vulnerability and the idea of true intimacy with other people. I was threatened by life in general. I would do anything on a physical plane. But if you asked me to get real on an emotional level, you'd most likely get punched, or I would just shut you out for good. To my mind, if I acted tough enough, no one would see through to the scared little person I was inside. It doesn't matter what exactly the behaviors look like when they manifest. They all come from the fractures and blocks of an unbalanced body/mind/spirit system.

Now about the intellect. Intellect is our worst enemy when it comes to fear; these two go hand in hand like flies on shit, and they're about as good for us as flies and shit. The smarter we are, the more power our minds can wield over us. The mind is always one step ahead of us when it comes to fear. After all, fear is a creation of the mind, so the mind knows your fear the best. It created it! Thus, the smarter we are, the harder time we are going to have getting a handle on the mind. I'm an example of this. I had to take myself to the edge of life, to where I had to die, in order to get a handle on my mind and my fears. I couldn't get the clarity without the death.

My mind is a weapon of mass destruction. It was always one step ahead of my soul, weaving the intricate web of stories, fears, and lies it had to weave to keep me going on the path I was walking; a path seeking numbness from all the pain and agony of living in a world I didn't understand. My mind was operating solo and out of balance, as it had no contact with my spiritual body, because there was complete blockages in my Vishuddha, or Throat Chakra. It's just like the U.S. government, which was designed the way it was so that no one department had too much power. Having learned from the monarchies and oligarchies of Europe the brilliance of the democracy as it was meant to be lived was that there were branches of government to keep the power in balance. (Of course we are now seeing a massive breakdown in design of our system, but just like communism, democracy worked in theory. Also a whole different topic for a whole entire book in itself!)

I lived in fear of breaking through this blockage my whole life, although like everything else we've discussed, I wasn't aware of it at the time. Under the surface, fear ruled my life to the point of destruction. Unbeknownst even to me, I wanted so badly to scream out and express my bottled up rage at life, but I was too afraid to let the emotions flow. It was as though I physically couldn't let them move.

Energetic blocks are quite real, let me tell you. As real as a brick wall. I just knew I wasn't going to get emotional even if I thought I might want to. I was trapped in an intellectual and mental prison. My ego-mind kept creating stories and fears to keep me in line, to keep me doing what it wanted, which was to numb the pain and keep me separate and disconnected. This was due to the fact that I believed my life should be comfortable and free of pain and discomfort. I believed this false inner narrative to the point of death.

I share this to illustrate the fact that in order to grow towards our true potential, we must push outside our fears. However, first we must balance our systems and unlearn our learned programing so the fears no longer have the power they once did over us. We will then come to find that when we live in a state of balance and energetic flow, we can see that nothing we once thought was the truth and nothing we once saw as a threat is actually real. It's all just a massive illusion created by the filters and programming of the mind. When we acknowledge this, we can break free from it.

"Always do what you are afraid to do." ~Ralph Waldo Emerson

Chapter 9
The Balanced Mind

"Happiness is not a matter of intensity but of balance,
order, rhythm and harmony."
~Thomas Merton

How do we come to balance? Balance is the natural state of the world and the universe. There must be balance. Things can only run in a state of unbalance for so long before balance must be restored, which the intelligence of all that is will work to restore if we cannot do it ourselves. This is true for us on an individual level as well as on a communal and global level. Mother Nature lashes out to restore balance. White blood cells do what they do to restore balance. Thus we see examples of the microcosm/macrocosm everywhere we look.

In balance, we can find a true state of happiness and peace. However, it's not a state that, once achieved, can be left unattended. Balance must be consistently and diligently maintained in order to be lasting. This is exactly where many people struggle, because, as a whole, we have become very mentally undisciplined. We have forgotten that diligent hard work and discipline are necessary for the payout of balance. We must put in energy to hold personal balance.

Over the course of time, humans have come to believe that we should reap the benefits after applying little to no effort. We believe that what we want should just be given to us. This is simply not the way of things. We want change but don't want to get uncomfortable or sacrifice anything to bring it about. For example, if I want the Zen peace of a Buddhist monk, or the equanimity and unconditional love and acceptance for all beings, even enemies, which we see embodied in the Dalai Lama or Thich Nhât Hańh, then I must *work* towards it. I must practice daily for a long time to reach and maintain this level of balance.

Yet, my programmed mind would have me believe that if I can't wake up with it after just one week of yoga, then why should I bother at all? That after one week of good eating, I should look and feel like my ideal body. When we find out it will take months, we often quit before the real change can take root. Does that ring a bell for you at all? I hope it helps illustrate my point. There are many ways to find balance, and, here, we will talk about the daily practices I use to maintain balance in my mind.

First, though, let us talk about what balance is. I like to visualize it as harmony, serenity, and acceptance. Peace.

A mental state where there is no friction and strife. A state where we respond appropriately to life as it is unfolding instead of reacting based on the filters of the past.

These are the realistic facts and ways of life when we are living in a balanced state within ourselves. In balance, we have no want for anything. We give to the world, and we take only what we need. We love unconditionally and have no need to force our will. We accept that whatever happens is meant to happen, and that we have no control over anything outside of ourselves. We accept any outcome with serenity and peace because we trust in the greater plan. We face our trials and our challenges with a smile and an open heart because we know that, on the other side, life is going to be a little more beautiful, and we will come out a little more fulfilled. We look for the lessons in everything, and we live in the present. Fear no longer runs the show and neither does ego. We have no need to cling and attach because we trust that we are complete and perfect in ourselves as we are meant to be...*in all of our flawed imperfections.* We no longer seek outside ourselves for fulfillment because we are aware that everything can be found within us. We see there is an energetic answer to all that is, and it can be found in our own beautifully balanced and flowing open chakra system and alignment of the body, mind, and spirit.

The balanced mind has no need, or space, for stories and fears. The balanced mind lives in the present moment and sees the moment for what it is at any given time, free from all those dirty, grimy filters that it looked through for so long. We must restore energetic balance to our chakra system in order to balance our minds. One cannot exist without the other.

It was when I woke up in yet another detox, after finally dying, that I was able to step back and observe just how unbalanced and blocked I had been. I remember what it felt like as I lay on the dirty bathroom floor convulsing after I shot a massive dose of really good cocaine into my arm. My heart was going to explode, or so it felt. The thunder was rushing through my head, and I was at peace. I would welcome this end to my physical existence; it had been nothing but torture anyway.

When I returned from the fog of the in-between, the world of the undead but unliving that we addicts dwell in, I finally saw myself through new eyes. I had broken free and made it back somehow alive. Part of me had indeed suffered death, but I was more gloriously alive than I had been in a very long time. I had successfully killed the mindset and filters which had been working overtime throughout my life–the chaotic, egotistical, and arrogant persona which had flourished out of the traumas, fractures, and blocks within me.

There I was, laying in the bed of yet another detox, broken, homeless, and all around lost, yet I felt reborn. I felt the infinite potential of my life even though I knew I had a massive amount of work to do. It was in that moment I made a commitment to myself and to God and the powers that be. As I lay there with my eyes closed, I felt the warm spring Southern California breeze, heavy with the scent of jasmine, on my skin and hair. As it caressed me, I felt a sense of deep peace I had not known since that day, almost

20 years earlier, when I took a fateful swig of SoCo on the Jersey shore and it teased me with the allure and promise of this peace, which it failed to deliver). I finally felt as though I was no longer at war with myself. I felt safe. I felt like I knew nothing. And, for the first time ever, it didn't matter. I no longer needed to know. It was my first taste of just simply being. It was my first sense of gratitude, as well as my first sense of connection to God and all that is. From that moment on, I approached life with a new childlike yearning to finally learn how to be a human. I didn't know what was ahead but I knew I no longer wanted the chaotic and aggressive existence I had. I became a seeker, and I sought out wisdom until I found what spoke to my soul essence.

Practices for Balance - Yoga

"Yoga is the journey of the self, through the self, to the self." ~Bhagavad Gita

Yoga is a practice that anyone can begin. Yoga is personal. It is a never-ending journey through all of our own walls, behaviors, thoughts, conceptions, misconceptions, beliefs, and ideals to a place where we find ourselves deep within, exposed, vulnerable, raw, and, above all, loved. It's a journey to the place of divine consciousness and interconnectedness where we detach from our limited identity with the physical form.

The thing about yoga is that there is no finish line. There is no ultimate asana that says we are a master. We are a yogi when we say we are. When we undertake a practice and begin to incorporate the practice of yoga in our life off the mat, than we are indeed yogis.

Once upon a time, in my unbalanced state, I started practicing yoga. I loved it, but I did not truly understand the deeper parts of it. I wasn't ready for the revelations back then. I knew I loved how it made me feel and that it kept my body toned and flexible, but I wasn't living my practice off the mat. I wasn't truly connecting with the essence of what yoga really is. I was competitive, and I would look around the room in comparison because, in my mind, I had to hold each pose better than the others, for longer, and more perfectly. Heaven forbid I fell out of a pose! Shame would kick in. Now, I love to fall out of a pose, because it shows me exactly where my mind is in that moment, and it shows me where I need to focus my breath and what I can work towards. It reminds me not to take myself or life so damn seriously! My yoga practice, on any given, day shows me exactly what area of my system might need balancing and cleansing, or where I am holding onto stuff emotionally and energetically.

When I started yoga, I struggled to hold any of the one footed balancing asanas because my system was still all kinds of unbalanced. How could I display balance physically when I was all sorts of unbalanced within? I lived in my head. I thought I could force the positions into being, and you better believe I tried to! I didn't know anything about the breath, pranayama, Chi - the Life Force. I didn't yet know that by breathing into the struggle, we could ease it. I approached yoga through my mind like I had with my whole life. In the beginning, I was still energetically fractured. My feminine energy was blocked. I was all ego and no emotion. Everything was still buried under a state of disinterest and bitterness. This is where we can begin to see how our energetic blocks manifest in the body. So maybe I could hold a right side asana, but not a left, since everything in the physical body has an energetic significance like we talked about earlier. Right side is linked to masculine while the left is linked to feminine.

Physical manifestations show up and hang around long after the energetic problem has occurred and taken root. I would shake, fall over, hold my breath, curse inwardly, and try to force the asanas I was struggling with. I would curse myself in my head. I wanted to be the best. You could say that I was completely missing the point. But I kept at it. I kept practicing. Yoga called to me as a path to freedom. In each practice I would experience a little taste of serenity, and I wanted more.

Now, I welcome the challenges of life, thanks in large part to my yoga practice. I appreciate the chance to breathe into the moments that are most trying. I don't always live up to my ideal, and that's ok too. These challenges show me that my mind is a liar because I can go on long after my mind tells me I can't, and I can walk through things my mind used to tell me would demolish me.

When something in life challenges me, I think of my yoga practice and the poses which challenge me most, and I breathe through the struggles. Instead of quitting, like my mind still wants to do some days, I go back to my breath just like I would in my yoga practice. In other words, I've become an observer. It feels quite magical when my mind kicks up and says, *"fuck this."* And instead of taking off and running away from the challenge, another voice speaks up and says, *"No, wait. Pause. Take a breath. Okay, one more. You got this. What are we here to learn?"* To a runner like me that new voice and my ability to listen to it sound like and make me feel like a superhero!

There are many different kinds of yoga. I encourage beginners to try out different practices to see which one speaks to their heart. Yoga taught me that it doesn't matter if I fall over. I can get back up and try again. Just like in life. It taught me that, with a little bit of hard work, breathing, dedication, discipline, and practice, I will continuously improve. I can always do better if I just try. It taught me that I can focus on what's in front of me in any moment, and my mind can be silent while I remain present in my body and the moment.

My yoga practice taught me to accept my body for whatever it is on any given day. It taught me to love me for me no matter how I am showing up. Those imbalances of the mind which manifest in the physical body still show up, and my yoga practice shows me what areas may need attention by how my body is responding in my practice on any given day. Yoga will quiet the mind so you can get in touch with your true nature within, your own true bodhichitta—your soft spot. This is the soft, vulnerable, divine space within each of us, which is the essence of our true nature.

Yoga is the place where my mind finds love, acceptance, and compassion for me in any given moment of any given day. It shows me exactly where I am physically, mentally, and spiritually. This allows me to, in turn, be a conduit of love and compassion for others.

Practices for Balance - Meditation

"Meditation is a way for nourishing and blossoming the divinity within you." ~Amit Ray

Meditation. The word just brings a smile to my face and a rush of love to my heart. Meditation is magic for me because it keeps me free from my mental prison. Like yoga, meditation is a never-ending, beautiful, self-searching practice. One which brings about infinite lessons, along with an endless supply of inner peace of mind that is always available for us to tap into. It's always there, we just don't know it until we discover it.

Until we begin looking within, we have no idea that what we have been seeking all along is right there inside. We can't see clearly enough until we have quieted the ego-mind and cleared away those dirty filters of our ego and subconscious that we've been perceiving the world through. Meditation helps us with this.

My life purpose is to bring balance to myself so that I can then help bring balance to the world through sharing my journey and teaching others about balance through chakra healing meditation. Naturally, I get all warm fuzzy, and excited when I hear meditation! The energy starts charging through me like someone turned on the lights. Introducing meditation to people who may have never considered it before, is my passion. This is why I have embraced my heart path which includes chakra teaching and healing work with others. (Learn more about my chakra programs in the resources section).

As a person who suffered deeply from a chaotic and addictive mind, which was the symptom of energetic fractures and blocks, I am proof that anyone can realign themselves with a bit of healing, discipline, practice, and love. I am proof that meditation fuels massive shifts in and alignment of the deeper root causes of disorder and dis-ease.

When I first got sober, I just wanted my head to be quiet. I wanted to stop obsessing about everything outside of my control. I wanted to stop thinking and judging everything. I wanted a quiet space where I could finally be enough. I wanted to stop beating myself up. I wanted to stop worrying and feeling anxious. I wanted to feel useful and whole. I wanted to love and be loved. I wanted to feel connection.

Funnily enough, as I sat with all of these desires in a detox center in Long Beach, California, a book found me. This book was written for prisoners doing hard time, and it was geared toward introducing a proper meditation and breathing practice to them. The way I saw it, it was perfect for me, because I was doing time in a sense. I dove into the book, and I started practicing pranayama breathing, or pran as the author called it. Pran simply is the breath, the Life

Force. Pranayama breathing is a controlled breath practice which stills us. It's a proper practice of deep breathing which frees energetic blockages; furthermore, it brings us to the here and now. It keeps us present in the body. This is where we start to tap into our life force.

There are many different breathing exercises to cleanse the system, but I started right then and there with what I had, making no more excuses about the right time or needing a teacher. I started a practice of visual breathing where I took in the love from the people who cared for me and visualized the light from it entering me. As I exhaled, I envisioned golden waves of gratitude for their presence in my life, and I imagined these waves flowing all the way across the country to them, back to New Jersey and Florida to my family. I tapped into the golden web of love and sat with it as I would breathe. When my mind would wander, I would say, *"thinking,"* and then just come back to my breath. Over and over again. This is how I learned to meditate. It's simple, and it successfully introduced a method of quieting my very chaotic mind.

I started very basic and simple, and I journeyed through many different teachings and practices until I found what worked for me personally. Each time I was ready to move to another level of practice, the teachings found me. They came into my path, via books and various people, to introduce a plethora of ideas and wisdom to me.

My practice is very much influenced by the Buddhist and Hindu traditions, with some New Age teachings mixed in as well. I am a student of Kriya Yoga as taught by my guru, Paramahansa Yogananda and his line of spirit, as well as a student of Thich Nhât Hanh and Pema Chödrön. I have developed my own practice of meditation that incorporates observation, devotion, energy movement, visualization, chanting, seed mantras, healing, and balance. This is what I now get to give to the world.

There are tons of different ways to practice meditation. Like yoga, I encourage seekers to find what speaks to them. You can read Thich Nhât Hanh and use his teachings of mindfulness practice and walking meditation. Open yourself up and the teachings will come. You can study Pema Chödrön and begin to practice maitri, or loving-kindness; or tonglen to learn compassion. You can meditate on your chakras and focus on energy and chakra healing. This is what I teach. You can sit in Zen meditation where you try to empty yourself of everything to see that in everything there is nothing. There is Vipassana, which teaches observation and non-reaction. There are guided meditations and nature walks.

The point I want to make is I have studied and practiced many, and have come to my own place of what I use in my practice because it works for me. And it absolutely works for me like nothing else I have ever known. Most of the time, I am able to live in a state of love and compassion that I once thought impossible. I now help people find their own path and practice of meditation, one which fills their own heart. I have discovered a place through my practices where I can tap into this energy at any time. It's a place of self-love, acceptance, compassion, non-reaction, non-judgement, understanding, and divine love. I have peace of mind, and a genuine mindset of love and goodwill for others. Instead of viewing the world through the dingy filters of my past experiences and my ego, meditation helps wipe the slate of my mind clean each and every day that I practice. It brings a freshness to my experiences, one where what happened yesterday doesn't matter and I am truly living in the present.

Meditation allows me to approach the world from a balanced state of mind, where I take each moment as it is, instead of what stories my mind is trying to tell me. Ask yourself if you're tired of the stories that your mind creates. If so, you are ready for a practice. This is where I have found true freedom.

I am no longer tied up in that back seat of the car while my ego-mind speeds towards that cliff we talked about. I am now a willing participant in my life and I am guided by my heart and soul–my link to the divine. I am a conscious co-creator of my reality instead of a victim of life. My mind no longer runs amok like an undisciplined 2 year old having a temper tantrum. Instead, my Higher Self is in command (most of the time), and when I do stumble and act like a fool, I love myself more for it because it's all part of my human experience. Through this practice, I am able to love each of you more too, despite the foolishness we can all exhibit as humans who get so stuck in our ways.

I offer a free 7-Day introductory meditation boot camp, which you can learn about here: http://hugyourchaos.com/meditation-boot-camp/

Practices for Balance- Outlets

"Music is therapy for me. It's my outlet for every negative thing I've ever been through. It lets me turn something bad into something beautiful." ~Amy Lee

My mind was insanity for most of my life, as we've already discussed in depth. It never stopped. The few occasions amongst the chaos where I can recall being at peace and in the moment, I was snowboarding or traveling. Those were the two things I found in life, in the midst of all the chaos, which showed me there was a better way to live. They are the two things that let me touch upon connection, how ever briefly they may have been. Those moments showed me there was indeed more to life than what I was living. I just didn't understand it at the time, and I certainly had no idea how to maintain it. I knew something was different in those moments, but I couldn't put a finger on what. Now I understand it was simply the connection.

To this day I remember what it was like before I was aware of the ever present energy flow and balance. Before I was connected, I was clueless. My head as a teenager was a very noisy, busy, chaotic, and judgmental place. It was hard on me and hard on everyone around me. But mostly me. On and on it would carry. No matter what I did or said, no matter what I wore or how I looked, I was never good enough. I was always scared, and my head was always telling me how stupid I would look if I did this, or how weak I would look if I showed that emotion. It seemed as though my mind would never give it a rest.

When I played sports, it was the ongoing narrative of, *"Don't mess up; don't mess up. If you mess up, you suck and no one is going to like you."* At school it was the constant, *"Don't say that. You are going to sound dumb. No one likes you anyway so why are you bothering?"* and, *"Why bother? You will never do it as good as this person anyways, and no one will like you if you aren't the best."* At home it was, *"Don't cry; don't complain. They aren't going to love you if you cry and whine,"* and, *"You aren't good enough. Nothing you do is good enough. You suck! You suck! You suck! No one loves you."* It *never* stopped. It was always judging. And I was the harshest judge of myself, first and foremost. In hindsight, it's no wonder I was prone to extreme inner anxiety as a child. With all of that chaos bobbing around inside me, I'm surprised I didn't end up as a serial killer instead of a junkie.

I know. It's exhausting isn't it?

It exhausts me just remembering what it was like, living with that mind. Needless to say, it's no wonder that I vividly remember finding the flow like it was yesterday. Of course at the time I didn't know it was 'the flow' per se, but I became aware that it was *something*. The first time I felt it, or that I was aware of being in the flow, I happened to be snowboarding, one of my all-time favorite activities. We were going up on the chair lift and I was thinking to myself, *"I wish I could feel like this all the time."*

I sat there and tried to explore the feeling of 'this' as I attempted to name exactly what 'this' was so that I could talk about 'this' with my friend. At 16 years old, I had zero knowledge of things spiritual, energetic, or esoteric, so I didn't know it was the flow I was in. I just knew my head was quiet and, for once, I wasn't beating myself up. I wasn't filled with doubt and insecurity. I wasn't afraid or threatened. I wasn't worried what everyone was thinking of me; and I wasn't worried about not being good enough or unlovable. I wasn't worried about tomorrow, nor was I hung up on something I did or said yesterday while beating myself up for its perceived stupidity. There was no stress. There was no judgement. There was just bliss. I just *was*.

My mind was quiet, content, and peaceful. It wasn't busy trying to figure out all the answers of what I was going to be in life, or how was I ever going to manage. It wasn't worried I would never find love. Nothing mattered but the very moment. Nothing was there but me, the breath coming out of my cold lips in a puff, nature all around me, and that cold, crisp feeling the air carries when it's about to snow. The snow glistening on the trees, white and sparkly, and it felt as though I could *see* everything for the first time. I heard the quiet hum of the chairlift motor as we ascended the mountain. The beautiful quiet in the air that comes before it snows pressed in all around us. It was one of those gray New Jersey winter days where the sky is cloudy but it's bright and crisp, as though the sun is trying to shine through but can't. Where it's cloudy but not gloomy. It's still so clear in my mind. I can taste it. The air was charged with an electricity I could not explain, but it felt good.

I sat staring at my feet, one strapped into the snowboard, and the other dangling free, as I tried to put words to my thoughts. I was never good at speaking up (there's that Throat Chakra issue again). When I tried, I felt like a bug under a microscope. I felt my most awkward and bumbling—anytime I tried to explain my inner thoughts and feelings, I was immediately embarrassed. There was so much shame attached to my emotions it was crazy. It was a little easier with my close friends, but not much. So I stammered out to Jen, "*Don't you just wish you could feel like this all the time? Like nothing in the world matters? Like it's all okay?*" And she sort of nodded and said, "*Yeah, I guess,*" as though she was thinking what did I really have to be worried about that was so heavy.

I'm guessing she didn't really get what I was feeling, but of course that's the difficulty with explaining anxiety, depression, and not quite right to someone who feels good in the world. She wasn't as heavy as me all the time. Her brain didn't seem to be on constant overwhelm all hours of the day, so the fleeting moment of peace that I was all jazzed about wasn't such a big deal to her. For me though, it was life-changing. It was reminiscent of the whisper of peace that bottle of SoCo had offered years before. From that moment on, I would spend years chasing the feeling of being in the flow without any understanding of what exactly it was, or where I could find it.

It would take me decades to realize that the feeling I was trying so hard to describe could be found within me and tapped into at any given time. It would take me almost 20 years to realize that meditation would bring me to the exact same place snowboarding did, and teach me to carry it with me as I faced the world. What I was experiencing in that moment was the same bliss and full awareness of the present…the one we can reach through meditation practice. This is an illustration of the benefits that constructive and healthy outlets have for us when striving to achieve balance. When we have things to do which make our hearts sing, regardless of what is happening in our world at the moment, these things help clear out our mind; they speak to our soul. Participating in these outlets is a wonderful way to give our mind a vacation because they anchor us in the present moment.

Maybe it's art or writing, sports or exercise, music or cooking. It doesn't matter what the activity is, so long as it puts your mind at rest and *connects* you to the now. In the space the activity creates, we are cleared of self-doubt and a space opens up for our heart and soul to shine through. It's the activities we feel at home in; the ones where we feel whole, good enough, powerful, strong, capable, at peace, present, and like a boss while we are doing them. It is the activities we must incorporate into a balanced life in order to play and have fun; these are essential!

Play doesn't have to be silly. Play can be anything which helps you feel free and clear. Ideally, if we can pursue our own heart path far and long enough, it will take us to a place where our passion becomes our work because we are serving our life's purpose.

This happens when we achieve a state of balance and alignment within. When we are balanced and aligned we find our life's purpose becoming quite clear to us, and the doors start opening to make our purpose become a reality. With all of those blockages and fractures in the system put to right and cleared out, we find we no longer have to force our will upon the world. We discover more conducive means for expending energy than exhausting our mind trying to figure out all the answers. We find the answers just flow in when we create the space to let them.

If you could get paid to do any one thing in your life, what would it be?

Fractured

Section 3
The Spiritual Body

.

Chapter 10
Reunification With the Spirit

"Our scientific power has outrun our spiritual power. We have guided missiles and misguided men." ~Martin Luther King, Jr.

Humanity suffers from a spiritual malady. We are so consumed with our human existence. Our distorted individual needs drive our every move and keep us so disconnected and out of touch with our spiritual body - our true nature - that we are completely losing track of what it is to be a human being. Yet, paradoxically, we are drowning in our own messy humanness. We are drowning in the power of the human mind, and, akin to a distorted, cancerous plague of emotionless robots, we are losing humanity to "I, me, and mine."

The realm of the spirit. The spiritual body, if you will. In the spiritual body there is only *right now*. Eckhart Tolle describes it best in his book, *The Power of Now*. By the time I read this, I had experienced the power of now and was so pleased to find someone putting my experiences into words. I mentioned connection earlier, and this is where I found mine!

When we align our three bodies - mind, body, spirit - with one another, we are living in the spiritual realm of completion and balance. When alignment occurs, energy flows, and magic can happen. When we come to the place of unity with mind, body, and spirit in balance, we come to a place of reconnection with our Higher Self and a connection with Source, the greater Collective Consciousness, God, and each other. When we can master the ego-mind in order to quiet it at will, we allow ourselves to be fully present in any given moment in the place of no-mind; this is living a spiritual existence. This is the place of enlightenment.

The spiritual body is the presence that is always there–just beyond the thoughts, beyond the emotions, and beyond the physical body. It's the place we touch when we can quiet our relentless mind enough to be in the now; the space deep inside where there is nothing and there is everything. It is the place of stillness and peace which overflows with an abundance of infinite divine love and eternity. When we can cut through all of the bullshit the mind creates–all of the illusions, all of the identities we cling to, all of our opinions, and divisions–and touch the place of inherent softness within, the one where nothing else matters but pure divine love, this is the spiritual body. It is the place where the beauty of what is occurring right in front of us is so amazing that we stay with it because we can finally appreciate how blind we have been throughout our lives. It's where we finally understand all is nothing, and nothing is all; we grasp the beauty of duality and paradox and we cease having a need to know.

The spiritual body is always there waiting for us to come back to it. Waiting for us to quiet the mind enough to reunite with it. It's patient. It waits, and does not judge. It is the observer deep within us all. It's the 'Higher Self' if you will, the inherent knowing and intuition, the sixth sense. We all have it, it's just a matter of reconnecting with it. That's the secret. The problem with us humans is that we seek outside of ourselves. We look to others for exactly what reconnecting with our own inner spirit can do for us. This is the human condition. Just as I did for so long on my own, humanity as a collective is suffering from a spiritual disconnection.

We have been bred and taught to believe the answers to all of our pain and problems can be found through an outside source. We have been taught pain is unacceptable and we should avoid pain at all costs, thus we see society as it is today–everyone attempting to avoid pain to the point they are no longer living but merely existing and hiding from life under the guise of security. I suffered from this malady for years. I believed there was something wrong with me because I felt so much pain and vulnerability, and I went on a mission to numb that pain. I didn't realize that, from a young age, as an empath part of my pain was that of the collective consciousness. I thought it was mine, and it was overwhelming. I didn't know what to do with it and no one was teaching emotional pain management in school.

Had I been balanced, or healed sooner in life, I may have come to this understanding then. However that wasn't my path, and I fully accept that. I am here now, which is what matters. Now. The blocks and disconnections of our past can be healed by simply going in and energetically balancing and working towards healing chakra system, which results in balance of the triad of mind, body, and soul. In my experience, as I've healed on an energetic level, it allowed my other ailments to correct themselves.

As we work on balancing, cleansing, and healing the chakra system we reconnect with the spiritual body. It's inevitable. The unity returns and we become clear. When this occurs we start to care less about our egoic need for identity, dualism, opinions, and beliefs. All these dense behaviors stop being important, and what starts to matter is love, peace, and joy. Ancient knowledge returns to us from the Collective as we clear out the festering old wounds and the mud of the past. We inherently know truths for what they are, and we begin see through the illusions created by the mind and by society. We want to help others, and we seek to understand rather than be understood. We seek to love, rather than be loved. We begin living the Prayer of St. Francis. We suddenly understand what it means to be a Buddha. We see the bigger picture, and we have an inner knowing that it is the truth of what we are. We suddenly connect with the answers we have spent years seeking outwardly.

This is not to say that we turn into blobs of nothing with no personality–that's just an extreme belief/fear created by ego. (Mine tried to tell me this!) We still have our 'identities' per se, but we see how they can change on any given day, and we allow it. We become flexible, content, and loving human beings. We no longer need to define the self, because there is no self. We are at one within, while fully realizing the self as we once saw it no longer exists, thus we reconnect with all existence.

It is a bit of a paradox, I agree. We are connected on a higher level to a greater consciousness, so we stop needing to define everything. There's a bigger picture at play, and it becomes quite obvious when we reach this point of our journey. It becomes the place where we don't want or need anything because we are completely immersed in the moment, and, in the moment, we want exactly what we have, so it cannot be a want if we currently have it in this moment, can it? Do you see what we create and how we avoid the moment? By constantly focusing on what we want, we are out of touch with what we actually have. It's a perpetual state of dissatisfaction, which is a sign of disconnection.

That's the awesome aspect with the spiritual connection–*everything* becomes a paradox. An irony. Yet it all seems to just make sense. We see the order in the chaos, and the divine in the darkness. We see how without the chaos there could be no balance, and without the darkness there could be no light. We understand that we have to have the pain to have the joy. Sound cannot exist without stillness. For us to exist there must also be empty space that is nothing. An object cannot be if there is nothing for it to come out of.

Once we accept the duality and truth of all that is as they are, there is no more struggle. We accept that nothing is static, everything must flow and change like the tides or the winds. We tap into the greater realm of Collective Consciousness and we realize that no matter what storm, rain, clouds, pain, flood, tornado, thunder, cyclone, or downpour is occurring at any given moment, it doesn't matter. It doesn't matter because we no longer attach to any of it. It doesn't matter because we finally get it. We see that behind it all, after all the storms, the infinite blue sky and sunshine of divine joy and love is there waiting for us to tap into it. When we get upset at the landscape or the weather, or the circumstances around us, this is because we are seeking for our surroundings to do for us what reconnecting with our spiritual body will do. We say, *"If only the weather were nicer, I would be happy."* This is false. When we are connected and balanced we are happy even throughout the storms.

This is when we return from a balanced state of presentness in the moment to an unbalanced state of mind, or ego. Because naturally we fluctuate. When we're non-accepting of the landscapes around us, the behavior or lifestyles of others, our own circumstances, or even ourselves, this is when we fall into resistance and suffering. The mind starts to say, *"I want this to happen,"* and when we attach to the outcome or idea and we don't get it, we create our own suffering. This is out of balance with the spirit.

The spirit inherently knows that things will go the way they will, and we can't always have what we want. The spirit understands everything happens the way it does for a reason—it sees the order in the chaos. It accepts that events play out in the way which best serves us at any given moment, so it happily floats through it, accepting whatever arises with grace and fluidity. It's when we are attached and identifying with the mind that we create the suffering. We can float back and forth between these states at any given time. Like I mentioned, everything is fluid, static, and impermanent.

When I found the Buddhist teachings on impermanence, they spoke to my heart as though I was hearing a beautiful song for the first time. It all made so much sense to me as I devoured the teachings on the nature of human suffering: how we cling to ideas and beliefs of how things "should" be, and when they don't stack up we are in pain. If we just accept things as they are, we find all is well and we are okay no matter what. This is the most excellent measure for gauging where we are at any given moment–how well are we accepting what is happening right now? Are we accepting it well because it is in line with what we are wanting? How would we respond if it was the opposite, or if the tide shifted another way? Can we still smile and be present, or do we slip into depression, worry, fear, anxiety, doubt, tantrum, or any other non-accepting behaviors?

Like I said, I can be anywhere along the spectrum at any given time. These days my level of non-acceptance is not very high–nor does it appear very often–but I am still human and I still slip into the unbalanced mind state at times. For me, the most common is the weather. *"It's too hot, too humid, it's raining and I want to go out..."* and as soon as it comes out of my mouth, I hear myself, and I see it. In criticizing the weather, I am coming from a place of mind and non-acceptance. Then I have a chuckle, and I thank God for the beautiful weather. You see? We do not have to be perfect, just willing to see and observe what it is we do, and where we do it, to make a start.

Once we shine the light on the darkness inside, the mindless programmed beliefs start to fade away. They cannot hold up in the light of mindful seeing. It is only when we hide them away in the dark and deny them that they fester and continue to plague us. In the light they fade, moving us further down the path of wholeness and balance. The more united and balanced we become–the more we accept ourselves, our flaws and idiosyncrasies–the more we accept everyone else too, because we see ourselves in everyone and everyone in ourselves.

"Our Generation has had no Great war, no Great Depression. Our war is spiritual. Our depression is our lives." ~Chuck Palahniuk

Chapter 11
The Imprisoned Spirit

"All the seven deadly sins are man's true nature. To be greedy. To be hateful. To have lust. Of course, you have to control them, but if you're made to feel guilty for being human, then you're going to be trapped in a never-ending sin-and-repent cycle that you can't escape from."
~Marilyn Manson

I believe, as a collective society, our minds have truly become dis-eased with addiction, and the addiction is thinking. I believe this goes for many more of us than just those we physically see struggling out in the open with the blatant manifestation of addiction to drugs and alcohol. The substance or behavior we choose to medicate the thought process with is merely a symptom–be it drugs, alcohol, sex, gambling, food, exercise, sugar, television, video games, social media, religion, over-analyzing, shopping, lying, labeling, judgment, jealousy, money, work, hoarding, or fear. That's the thing–all of these behaviors are the same; they are rooted in disconnection.

While obvious addictions like drugs, alcohol, or gambling cause more destructive problems for everyone involved, the root of the addiction is quite the same as the root of addiction in the person who overeats to avoid pain. It's no different than the person who works like a madman to make money, clinging to the idea that he/she just needs more money. The one who just needs to lose more weight to feel right, so they binge and purge. It's all devoted to drowning out the noise in our heads. It attempts to quiet the incessant voice inside that needs something to make us whole, complete, better, more secure, and happier—the voice that says the solution to our pain is just over there.

Think of it like this. Those of us who choose drugs or alcohol as the numbing/quieting agent are just choosing the fast track to destruction—be it destruction of the ego, destruction of the inner narrative that drives us mad, or destruction of the physical body in death. Addiction to drugs and alcohol is the high speed bullet train to the deep enough depths of pain which may facilitate a motivation to change, while behaviors such as egotistical labeling, judgement, or jealousy are more of a slow bicycle ride to the same deep enough misery that serves as a catalyst for change. It's like choosing to speed on the highway or put along slowly. Do you want to gallop or take a slow trot? I've always been an adrenaline junkie, so naturally I wanted it as hard and fast as possible. Thus, my spiritual disconnection manifested in the worst possible addiction there is–IV drug use. All forms of spiritual disconnection stem from the same root blockages and take us to the same place, just at different speeds.

From my experiences with various addictions, the substance or behavior we choose is a symptom of the deeper problem. The deeper problem is the disconnection from the spirit, the soul. The disconnection from Source energy - God. My dis-ease of addiction came from the energetic fracture within. I was so blocked and there was no flow of energy so I just couldn't connect. I became addicted to things outside of myself, and behaviors which skewed out of control and caused more suffering. The mind grows out of control because our spirits are locked away and there is no heart medicine to balance the intellect.

There is a lack of balance in society right now, individually and collectively. In my opinion, there is very little unification of mind, body, and soul. As a whole, we are too attached to identifying with one particular body; we can't see past our own limited physical or mental identity. This clinging to the identity of the physical body or the mental ego-mind arises from the energetic blockages and fractures which close off our connection to Spirit. We can't see past the idea that we are only our physical form; the fear of not existing beyond that realm consumes us. We fear losing the body because we don't see and believe that there is *so much more.* We cling to our egotistical, mind created beliefs, and social programming because we feel incomplete and inadequate.

In myself and others, I've seen how the mind tells us something and we believe it as the end all be all, the final word, because we so badly need that identity that I mentioned earlier. We become our thoughts, and if anyone tries to tell us differently, we bristle, and we are so offended. Our thoughts then form our realities and thus we end up stuck in self-defeating patterns of living.

For example, these days sometimes I can be so blissed out, present, aware, mindful, loving, tolerant and kind, that someone could come along and steal my wallet, and I might say, *"Wow, well I guess he needed that today, I am glad I could help"* and just accept it since there's nothing I can do about it. Now, the very next day the same thing can happen and based on my state of balance (or lack of), I might freak out, take it personal, and plot revenge for the next hour. What I always come back to is this: *it doesn't matter.* All that matters is now. Everything I no longer have need of, every self-limiting belief has been burned away, discarded, and let go of, so I may live in an enlightened state of balance *when I choose to remember and practice this.* I can also choose the state of human messiness and emotional chaos at any given moment, but that's the joy of being human, isn't it?

Presently, I see unfolding in humanity the exact drama that was my individual path in life. I unconsciously chose, over and over again, to serve myself and to take the easier way out every time I was challenged. Every thought my mind whispered, I believed. There were times through all of the darkness that I felt the presence of my spirit, but I just didn't understand how or what it was to connect with it. I was too clouded and heavy with dense negative energies to see clearly. I was trapped in delusions and selfish rationalizations. I was a victim of life.

I couldn't touch the inner knowing that would occasionally try to get my attention through all of the muck and ego I was carrying. In hindsight, I see my choices and how they went against my own spirit and best interests, but, at the time, I had no idea or ability to see I was indeed making choices, and bad ones at that. It didn't feel like I was choosing. I simply thought and believed that I was just living my life as I saw fit, based on what I knew, which I thought was everything, but, as it turned out, was very, very little. I was convinced I had all the answers and was so attached to the identity my mind was creating that I would have fought anyone who tried to tell me otherwise. In fact, I did fight often. I loved to argue. Remember, I had a hardcore need to make others wrong so I could tell myself I was superior.

My spirit was a prisoner of my ego-mind for a very long time. For most of my life, if I'm honest. The loud, incessant, mean, judgmental voice in my head was running the show for all those years and was the very one which had my true spirit imprisoned inside. If you've ever felt like you were doing something against your own will, knowing inherently it was against your own best interests, but doing it anyway, then you will understand what I mean here—this is an example of where I am going with this. Call it intuition, knowing, sixth sense, gut instinct—it's all the same. The little voice crying inside every time I said "fuck it" and reached for the needle or the crack pipe one more time. It was that little voice that I eventually buried deep enough inside until I couldn't hear it any longer as I stumbled blindly down my path to hell. It was that very voice I was trying to drown out with my submersion into the world of drugs and alcohol—the one whispering deep within my heart that there was more to life, a better way to live, and how I was capable of so much more than how I was living. My mind just wouldn't allow me to believe that. And my mind was the boss and jailer while my spirit was locked away inside.

Before very long in my earthly existence, I was so tired of the battle between mind and spirit…not that I understood that's what was happening. I just knew there was something 'not quite right.' Once upon a time, I had believed in myself and that anything was possible, that I could do anything I put my mind to. My spirit was in there, and it knew I was capable and worthy of doing wonderful things back when I was a child and could still hear the whispers of possibility it offered. The spirit always knows this, as it is part of our divinity and the greater consciousness. The spirit knows that we are of grace, and that we are pure love and light–a piece of the great Source in a manifested human form on Earth. On a deeper level, the spirit also knows that we chose to come to Earth to have a human experience, and that we have a purpose to fulfill, but the human mind forgets this and must live life to learn the lessons we signed up for.

I could hear the whispers of my purpose early in life. I believe I got messed up when my energies were thrown off and couldn't flow properly. My chakra system became blocked, fractured, and thrown off balance, and, thus, I became mired in my dense human emotions, thoughts, physical body, and experiences. What happened with me happens with so many of us–the mind takes over to help us survive, it gets out of control, and we either intellectualize or emotionalize everything for defense. I see it so often in my clients, friends, and people I've met and worked closely with during recovery from addiction. It seems to me that the natural human tendencies get out of whack, and we become prisoners of our own distorted behaviors.

Early on in life, we suffer trauma or pain, and the ego grows in response to this. Trauma and pain are to the ego what water or food is to a gremlin after dark. (If you don't get this analogy, your first assignment is to go watch *Gremlins*. Now.) The gremlins multiply when wet and the ego starts building up walls, because the ego knows that connection with the spirit, each other, and greater consciousness is a direct threat to its power and control.

Thus, the ego fights against anything which will balance us or unify our triad of mind, body, and soul. The ego is like the greedy dark Sith Lords in *Star Wars*, while the spirit would be the Jedi. You see, we have the potential within ourselves to go either way just like Anakin did when he chose the dark side and became Darth Vader. It's all a mirror of dualism and potentiality. What happens with the Force? Well, there must be balance in the Force, just like there must be balance within the mind, body, soul triad that makes each of us who we are.

In my experience, the physical body suffers from illness and dis-ease because of our unbalanced energy, and we are then distracted by our sicknesses and dis-eases. We attach to and identify with our illnesses, using them to make an identity for ourselves. We attach to problems, complaints, self-created dramas, and suffering. And how quickly we forget the whispering we once heard–the whispering from our spirit calling us to our true purpose amongst all this chaos. We forget it. We lose it in the noise, in the thinking, in the physical pain, but it is always there waiting for us to quiet down and listen. Once we reconnect to spirit we can once again hear it and use it to help us overcome our self-created pain, suffering, and dis-ease.

When I was a kid, I wanted to be a lawyer, a cowboy, a teacher, an acrobat, a figure skater, a doctor, and a helper. Probably not in that order, but those are the ones I remember most.   I just wanted to help anyone and everything. Helping was the calling of my heart and spirit. When we go back to childhood and touch on the pure intention we once had, this can help us get back into touch with our spirit. Remembering the pure potential and delight of the child mind serves as a key to our freedom.

What I have come to understand is this: even the most suffering amongst us, those we would label as 'evil', would have had a place in their childhood where they were still of pure intention, before their blocks and fractures became so extreme that they developed in the world as mass murderers, tyrants, psychos, and the like. After all, what is true evil but unenlightenment and ignorance? It's all just rooted in very deep suffering which grows from disconnection as it manifests in various ways and extremes. Maybe it's buried deep underneath layers of defenses formed to protect from the trauma and pain of abuse, or buried deep underneath years of hardened anger and resentment, but I truly believe that this pure spirit is there in all of us.

Having walked in darkness and in light, I am now able to see and understand the greater picture at hand. We all have within us the potential to go either way because all it really comes down to is energy. The spirit body is the energetic body. It is knowing and intelligent, but it is energetic. You can't see it, but, when tuned in, you can feel it.

I now understand that to walk the path of darkness, or 'evil', is merely a choice to stay and live in the lower density of extremely distorted human emotions. To choose the physical self over the spiritual collective can distort into evil very easily. To choose evil is to choose fear, hate, ignorance, greed, and power…to choose dominance and destruction of the Earth over our greater unity. To turn a blind eye to the suffering of others for the satisfaction of our own greed is to choose evil in the sense that it is fear based and ignorant to do so. To know better but not do better is a form darkness. To choose the light is merely a choice to raise one's vibration to the higher density energies of love, compassion, and tolerance. We do this by turning a light on in the darkness within us.

The higher vibration is always there waiting for us to return to it. If we can stop for a moment and imagine ourselves at our very worst moment—the moment we might look at and say, *"Wow, that was me living like that?"* *"Yikes, that is not how I want to be,"* then we can see that we have the potential to be as awful as the person whom we just passed judgement on.

However, we also see how we can be as loving or as enlightened as the Buddhist monk or Catholic saint. These days, I have so many of those moments in my life, and I keep them close to my heart for when my ego wants to sneak in and judge someone for their behavior. I used to beat myself up over my decisions, but no longer. I have forgiven myself because it does not matter; it is the past, and I was doing the best I could at the time and I can't change it. I can only do better now that I know better. I have relinquished my need to pass judgement on myself or others, which naturally results in forgiveness. Now my past behaviors are merely points of reference, and points of measurement to see where I am along the scale of being balanced and complete on any given day. They serve as beautiful reminders of where I came from, and where I can potentially return to if I sink back into complete imbalance.

For years, I chose to live against my own best interests as a drug addict and raging alcoholic. Despite my seemingly utter lack of choice in each moment of the darkness, I now firmly believe there absolutely was choice. I was just too consumed and disconnected to make the choice. Every time I stuck the needle in my arm, it felt as though another little piece of me died. Each time I thought about whether or not I should steal something to support my addiction, and I chose to go ahead and take what wasn't mine, I felt a little worse inside.

Each time I selfishly walked away from another family gathering to go score some dope, I felt myself fracturing, more and more, from the pure little soul I remember being as a child.

I will never forget the Easter Sunday when I left my aunt and uncle's house under the lie that I was going to see an old friend. My parents made me take my little brother with me, thinking this would ensure I was really going to the friend's house. They knew by this point what I was doing. I pleaded and lied, got the car keys, and instead forced my brother to take me to Newark to get some dope. I then strolled into the Little City housing Projects in my Easter Sunday dress and heels, a white girl sticking out like a sore thumb in the hood, thinking herself invincible, to score what I needed to get. I then proceeded to climb into the back seat and slam my dope, while telling my brother not to look back at me, to just keep driving.

It breaks my heart what I did to the people around me and to myself. But that's just what happens when we are stuck in the cycle; it's the insanity of living a fractured life. I was a prisoner of myself, and I don't know if there is a worse place to be than locked up inside yourself. Addiction is an issue that there is so much to be learned about, and it can get people very fired up. There is massive judgement, misunderstanding, and stigmatism attached to addiction. I am just sharing my experience with it. I claim no expertise but my own life and what I've come to understand about the spiritual nature of the root causes of my own addiction struggles.

Nobody forced me to do any of it but myself. I hear people get so angry and vicious towards those suffering from addiction, and, yes, I understand that their anger is fueled by their own misunderstandings and filters which color their view on the problem. But the anger and blame is never going to help anyone with anything.

I guess that's what I wish for people to understand; I know that addiction is one of the most selfish traps out there. I have a very great personal understanding of the fact that it causes destruction, ruining other people's lives besides the one who is addicted. But there is still a human in the addict too. There is a lost little broken human being inside the beast, one who is deeply suffering, and who is beating his or herself up more than anyone else could possibly do. It's an endless cycle of torture and pain, or destruction and madness. It's true insanity. And to think it all stems from spiritual disconnection.

The fact that today's society struggles so deeply to offer compassion to the suffering amongst us shows me that we have a massive spiritual disconnect across the board. What we seem to forget is that we can offer kindness and compassion without condoning something. We can operate from a place of non-judgement.

For example, each time a loved one would scream at me, *"Why can't you just stop?"* it was like nails on a chalkboard for me. I was just as angry and frustrated at myself as they were, if not more so. I was beating the shit out of myself every single moment for becoming such a horrible shell of a person way more than anyone else was because it went against everything I knew of myself in my spirit. I was the one—my ego-mind—who locked up the kind, peaceful, loving little soul I once was and dragged her down a path to hell because I couldn't stand to feel my emotions and frustrations at being so limited in this life. Because I just wanted a connection and didn't know where to find it.

I didn't understand that the chaos in my head was a symptom of spiritual disconnect, and I certainly didn't know how to quiet it. Over and over again, I chose to run towards what seemed safe instead of trying something different. And I realize this more than anyone else. There's a reason these memories are so clear to me–certain times when I was clearly at a crossroads, and I made the decision to go against my soul and do what my mind was saying and go back to getting high and running away. I can still connect with the moments that the break was occurring as I stepped further away from my spirit.

I can play these moments like a movie reel, and I see myself standing there in the hospital the time my parents dragged me out in my pajamas to force me to go to a detox. It builds up suspense as I reconnect with the inner war that was raging through it all–as my heart says, *"Quit, take the help,"* and my head says *"Run"*–and there comes that defining moment when I choose, one more time to run because that heart voice just wasn't loud enough. I listen to the big ego-voice in my head saying *"Run,"* and it's all in slow motion. The head can be so loud when it's running the show of imbalance. The heart stands no chance. In my memory though, I hear my heart cry *"Nooooo"* and off I go, out into the cold, snowy New Jersey night where I hide out by some Christmas lights in a churchyard after finding a pay phone to call for a ride.

As if watching a movie, in that moment, I hear the cell doors clang shut on my soul as I imprison my spirit once again. Those are the memories of my past life–the ones I remember not to punish myself over, but rather to use as motivation on the days I think that maybe I don't have to practice balance. They are the memories and experiences I can share with others to show that there is hope for all of us.

When I was 31, I walked away from someone I loved, outside of my immediate family, because I just wanted to keep getting high. My heart broke a little bit more that day, what was left of it by that point anyway, when I chose once more to immerse myself in the madness. See, I had built a little life for myself then, one I was sort of happy in…or at least I was as close to happy as I could have been at that point. I was the closest thing to happy I'd ever been.

I had a partner, I had freedom, I had joy, and fun. But I still just felt like I was missing something; that not quite right feeling persisted. It felt like I was living someone else's life. I liked it, I enjoyed it, and I loved the man I was with, but the life just didn't feel like mine. It was still somehow empty. It felt like a safe little shelter of existence. There was no fulfillment in it except when I would get to travel and snowboard, which goes back to those times I mentioned earlier—those outlets which brought about enough space within myself for me to reconnect with my spirit. And I would feel at home and all right in those times, but always with the cloud hanging just overhead knowing I had to leave that space and go back to my life. This is because I was still spiritually disconnected, only I had no idea!

Oh to have known then what I know now! To have discovered that I could have released the feelings within me at any time, because all they were missing was the alignment of my body, mind, and soul to put me in the present moment and to allow me to release. It was simply connection that was missing. It's so simple in hindsight, but God did I sure complicate the shit out of everything back then. And I still can being that I'm still a chaotically, messy human; it just no longer has the power over me it once did.

To further illustrate the suffering caused by a disconnection from the spiritual body, I will share this. Over the periods of my life when I wasn't strung out on heavy drugs, I was living as a "functioning" drunk—functioning as in I had a job, car, money, boyfriend, and all that "stuff" that we claim as being evidence of success. Yet I barely took a breath where I wasn't under the influence of at least a couple high-end beers. And I was miserable! All of the outward stuff that my mind believed would make me okay, I had. Yet I was still miserable and incomplete. I was still empty and not quite right; I just thought it meant there was something inherently wrong with *me*.

Little did I know, I was still not balanced and aligned with my spirit. So instead of drug addicted, I was drunk, ambitious, greedy, judgmental, sarcastic, bitter, cold-hearted, and a workaholic—all those lovely things I described in the section on mind—because I was still suffering from a metric shit ton of blocked energy. I was still majorly fractured.

I remained that way for a long time. I've spent time in all walks of life and dualities. I have been battle-hardened and soft. I have been mean, and I have been kind. I have been lazy, and I have been hard working. Stingy and generous. Loving and hateful. Selfish and selfless. Skinny and fat. Depressed and happy. Stagnant and fluid. Rigid and flexible. I can go on and on. The list doesn't end. The paradox of our dual natures is endless and a topic for an entire book in itself. The point is this, now I no longer *need* any of these labels to satisfy my identity, where once I relied on them and defended them as though my life depended on them!

This is probably why I can and will continue to empathize with those who are currently trapped and buried under their own fractured blocks, which manifest as darkness in all of its forms. As an empath, I feel the pain of others and I remember what it was like to be lost in that darkness, not knowing anything while I blindly groped and staggered through my existence, delusionally thinking that I actually had it all together and that everyone else in the world had it all wrong. I believe the spirit knows we must walk certain paths in order to gain certain experiences so we can achieve understanding and enlightenment. I believe in reincarnation, and that the more lifetimes we have lived on the Earth, the more stored wisdom we are able to tap into once we get clear.

The Akashic Records are there, waiting for anyone to tap into the infinite information bank of all that has been, all that is, and all that ever will be. (For an excellent book on this, see the resource page at the back of the book). We can choose to change at any given time, but, unfortunately, as human nature goes, it usually takes severe suffering to serve as a catalyst to shock us enough to wake up and invoke a deep paradigm shift. But, ultimately, I do believe we get to choose when we are ready.

Without my path being what it was, I don't know how long it would have taken for me come to this place of compassion and love that I am blessed to live in now. Maybe I would not have awakened in this life, but would have instead been forced to reincarnate again to repeat the cycle and to live through new and different human experiences aimed towards pushing me in the direction of awakening and evolution which would result in balance and unification of my mind, body, and soul.

Without my path, I never would have been able to see life for what it was or to understand the bigger picture. I would still be in the illusion of no choice, victimhood, and suffering–the wheel of samsara as we learn in Buddhism. During our human experience, I believe we always have choices–free will–and our choices either keep us in the illusion thinking we are safe and warm, or they rocket us towards a higher dimension to shatter the illusion of security, burning away everything we once thought we were and smashing all the beliefs which no longer serve us in our enlightened state.

I do believe I was meant to awaken and come to balance and connection in this incarnation because I believe that it is my purpose to help others on their own journey. I believe we all come here to live out an experience whose end result is to forge reconnection. Had I not come to awaken when I did—sitting in that detox in Long Beach, California on May 10, 2014—I believe I would have kept undergoing the severe suffering I was choosing.

My near death experiences towards the end of my addiction served as a catalyst for my paradigm shift. It's like we hear over and over–the lessons will repeat themselves in our lives until they have taught us what we need to know. If we aren't open to learning from them they will continue to show up until we do. Had I not underwent the profound shift in my consciousness while sitting in detox, most likely I would have went out and created more suffering for myself until I destroyed my physical body in death, thus being doomed to another new lifetime of suffering until that needed connection took root.

Due to the nature of the multiple near death experiences I underwent during early 2014, I firmly believe that we won't leave the Earth until our purpose is served. Each time that I went to the crossroads of life and death, under the fog of 'too big a dose,' something pulled me back to my body despite the fact that I really wanted to die. What can that be but the spirit body keeping us tethered to the physical body because it knows we have a purpose? The mental body may want death but the spirit knew it was not yet time.

My spirit tried to speak to me through the years. Forces were at play that planted seeds along the path. When I was 20, I was fresh out of yet another rehab, I was writing my heart out and getting reconnected with my soul. I was getting in touch with friends again and starting to think there was perhaps a life for me. A Buddhist book came into my path, and I started reading. At the time, music was my therapy and the powers that be were talking to me through song. There was a whisper of that paradigm shift, a slight breath of a shift in consciousness. At that point, I came to a crossroads and there I had a choice. However, there was still too much disconnection, fear, and ego running the show and I had no one to talk to of matters so deep as this. I still didn't understand; thus, the soil was not yet fertile enough for the shift in me to really take root. And so, I did not choose to water and nurture the breath of consciousness, the seed of enlightenment.

I instead chose to put the book down, withdraw from my poetry, music, and friends, and to return the way I had come, back to what I knew, back into my addiction. Why? Because it was comfortable. It was my comfort zone, and I had not yet learned to allow my spirit body to be heard. I listened to my ego-mind, and my head was getting loud again. I didn't see that I had to wade through the discomfort for a bit, watering the seeds of change in order to get to a state of peace. I didn't know how to walk through the pain and the uncomfortability of the places that scared the shit out of me. It all just seemed too difficult. I let my mind back in the driver's seat once again, and off we went back down the road to figurative and literal hell—or, as New Jersey knows it, Newark—for almost 12 more years of intense and grueling pain and suffering.

Herointown.

I had to return to the life of suffering until I really was dying. I had to suffer until that day in 2014 when I killed myself. The day I killed myself was May 10th and I remember it like it was yesterday, the day I agreed to give up my life one more time, and go to that detox. I had been dying a slow painful death for months at that point, not to mention all the times I fell unconscious on the floor after fixing myself. After a week of internal should I stay or should I go now, I got on the plane from Mammoth Lakes, California, to LAX after shooting 3 grams of cocaine in just as many hours. I was out of my mind at that point. As I downed glass after glass of Merlot and handfuls of OxyContin like candy, I felt it. I felt myself die. I knew that it was finally over.

All that I thought I was and all that I was clinging to–my ego, my belief that I knew anything–it all died on that plane flight. When I stepped off in LAX I barely knew where I was, I was defeated–like a garden after a tornado tears through–I was torn apart, uprooted, and being pushed through by energies greater than those of my physical body or mental capability. I was being propelled forward by my spirit body, a piece of the Divine, and by God. It was as though I was a wisp on the wind of the greater consciousness and some divine force was carrying me through the airport to where I found my ride.

That night, I went to sleep in death with the sweet and comforting smell of the night jasmine wafting across my room. And when I woke up a day and a half later, it was the start of a new life, a whole new journey. I was no longer stubborn, rigid, intellectual, and hardened. I was cracked wide open and willing to do whatever it took to change. I found myself to be open to a new way of life with a hunger I had never know. In that moment, the first reconnection of my body, mind, and soul was forged.

"Whatever is rejected from the self, appears in the world as an event."

~ C.G. Jung

.

Chapter 12
Spiritual Connection & Freedom

"We cultivate love when we allow our most vulnerable and powerful selves to be deeply seen and known, and when we honor the spiritual connection that grows from that offering with trust, respect, kindness and affection." ~Brene Brown

All this talk about spiritual disconnection and imprisonment is some heavy stuff! The most beautiful part of it all is that no matter where you currently are, there is hope for you to establish a connection beyond anything you could've imagined possible in this life. And the really good part? Is that the answers are so, so simple. You don't need a degree or anything else to align and balance your mind, body, and spirit so you can forge a reconnection in your life. You just have to *want* the change enough to put in some action!

The thing about the aspects of balance are that, no matter if we're talking mind, body, or soul, all the practices go together. All of the practices, such as yoga, pranayama, meditation, and creative outlets that I discussed in the other sections are crucial to balancing us on the spiritual plane, as well.

The one crucial element to spiritual reconnection that we haven't yet discussed is the one activity that lies at the crux of the teachings of Jesus, many world religions (when you clear out the dogma), and many 12-step recovery programs. I take no credit for this as it is not my answer to the spiritual problem. Have you guessed it yet? SERVICE! Service to our fellow beings and service to the world. When I was just coming into the realm of spiritual living, I knew I had *a lot* of healing to do before I would be free of the weight and guilt of my past. I felt, on the deepest soul level, the wounds of my life as they bled, raw and festering.

A wise lady told me that my soul was wounded and that service heals the soul. I took what she said to heart because I knew I was in serious need of some soul healing. The message was further delivered when I attended 12 step programs and heard again that to clear myself of self, which was the problem, I needed to serve others. As I continued seeking and became a student of Kriya Yoga and Tibetan Buddhism, I heard again how the problem with us humans is that we get so stuck in the self (and, in certain schools of Buddhism, the self doesn't actually exist so we must clear ourselves of this illusion to be free.)

Therefore, the solution is very simple, we just have a knack for complicating the shit out of life. When we are caught up in our selfish and egotistical desires (a symptom of the ego-mind), we suffer. When we are unbalanced in our chakras, the energies get stuck and stagnant, and we start living a life of disconnected pain and suffering which comes out sideways in any way possible (behaviors, dis-ease, illness, etc.). We cannot reconnect with our spiritual body when we are blocked by the stagnant, dense energy blocks of unhealed trauma, pain, resentment, anger, guilt, shame, remorse, jealousy, envy and so on. We must free ourselves from holding on to these emotions. Notice I did not say don't feel them. I simply said allow them to be released. Do not cling to them.

By practicing forgiveness, gratitude, compassion, and unconditional love–starting with ourselves–we cultivate the fertile soul for the spirit body to take root and forge a lasting connection in order to help maintain the state of balance we so desperately need.

"We cannot live only for ourselves. A thousand fibers connect us with our fellow men; and among those fibers, as sympathetic threads, our actions run as causes, and they come back to us as effects."
~Herman Melville

Fractured

Conclusion

First and foremost, if you or someone you know is struggling with addiction or depression I write to give you hope. There is help out there if you want it. I highly recommend 12 step recovery programs and have included some resources in the next section. It is my belief that through a combination of modalities, we can live normal, healthy and productive lives aligned with our own true heart path. Find the tools that work for you and use them. I would be doing you a disservice if I didn't acknowledge that 12 step programs were integral in the early stages of my healing and recovery. I live by the principle of anonymity so that is all I will say about that.

It is my truest hope that this book inspired you in several ways. One, to own and share your own story in order to help and inspire others. It is only our stories that we truly have. Our experiences are what shape our lives and are exactly what we come here to Earth to have. It is when we heal and we stop defining ourselves with what has happened to us that we truly find freedom and empowerment.

Two, to jump start your own healing journey if you are still living your own personal Dark Night of the Soul. It can end whenever you choose. Free will is real. The suffering stops with a decision on your part. Help is out there if you truly want to change. It's no matter if you choose my programs with Hug Your Chaos or someone else's.

I believe that the people we are meant to help will come to us when the time is right. This allows me to live in peace knowing that my story will find those it was meant for, just as the stories I needed found me when I was ready.

And three, to see yourself as a multidimensional being if you don't already. Expanding your mind beyond the limitations of the 3rd dimensional physical realm will be one of the most powerful choices you make. But get ready because there's no turning back once you know! You can heal yourself through energy, and whether that's through HYC chakra programs, empowerment programs, Reiki, crystal healing, Yoga, meditation, religion, or whatever you choose that works for you, it doesn't matter! Just choose. And start taking action.

The entire mission behind Hug Your Chaos was to spread the understanding that we are creatures of duality and paradox. It's when we stop trying to be this or that, right or wrong, good or bad, that we transcend this limited version of what we are. It's okay to have darkness because darkness is nothing more than the absence of light. This says that in darkness we have potentiality for the light to exist. When we accept this fact we understand that we are not inherently "good" or "bad", we just *are*. We are blank canvases that can be designed into anything at any moment. The idea with Hug Your Chaos is that we have to first acknowledge those things we want to ignore in order to heal from them! We must acknowledge them and give them a great big hug! That's the road to healing.

If you are really ready to amplify your healing work then come and visit www.hugyourchaos.com and find out more about the healing modalities and coaching programs we offer. If you're reading this book, it's for a reason, so who are you to ignore providence? Come see if we can help you grow your wings and fly!

Resources

Emergency resources:

SAMHSA (Substance Abuse and Mental Health Services)
Hotline - 24/7 help:
1-800-662-HELP (4357)

Alcoholics Anonymous (for help with an inability to stop
drinking) https://www.aa.org/pages/en_US/is-aa-for-you

Alcoholics Anonymous 24/7 hotline:
510-839-8900 for English
510-502-8560 for Spanish

National Suicide Prevention Lifeline
1-800-273-8255

If you or someone you know is struggling with depression,
addiction, anxiety, or wondering if you have a problem
with any of these, see the links below for free resources.

www.drugabuse.com
www.drugabuse.gov
https://www.recovery.org/
http://hugyourchaos.com/tag/addiction/
http://hugyourchaos.com/category/dark/

Suggested Readings to complement your work

"The Places That Scare You" by Pema Chödrön

"Start Where You Are" by Thich Nhât Hanh

"Anger: Wisdom For Cooling the Flames" by Thich Nhât Hanh

"Living Buddha, Living Christ" by Thich Nhât Hanh

"The Last Alchemist" by C. Jon. Sawyer

"The Four Agreements" by Don Miguel Ruiz

"The Alchemist" by Paulo Coelho

"Autobiography of a Yogi" by Paramahansa Yogananda

"Way of the Peaceful Warrior" by Dan Millman

53078261R00107

Made in the USA
Columbia, SC
14 March 2019